REVISE PEARSON EDEXCEL G

Statistics

REVISION WORKBOOK

Series Consultant: Harry Smith

Author: Navtej Marwaha

- -

Also available to support your revision:

Revise GCSE Study Skills Guide   9781447967071

The **Revise GCSE Study Skills Guide** is full of tried-and-trusted hints and tips for how to learn more effectively. It gives you techniques to help you achieve your best – throughout your GCSE studies and beyond!

Revise GCSE Revision Planner   9781447967828

The **Revise GCSE Revision Planner** helps you to plan and organise your time, step-by-step, throughout your GCSE revision. Use this book and wall chart to mastermind your revision.

For the full range of Pearson revision titles across KS2, KS3, GCSE, Functional Skills, AS/A Level and BTEC visit:
www.pearsonschools.co.uk/revise

Published by Pearson Education Limited, 80 Strand, London, WC2R 0RL.

www.pearsonschoolsandfecolleges.co.uk

Copies of official specifications for all Pearson qualifications may be found on the website: qualifications.pearson.com

Text and illustrations © Pearson Education Ltd 2018
Typeset and illustrated by Tech-Set Ltd, Gateshead
Produced by ProjectOne
Cover illustration by Miriam Sturdee

The right of Navtej Marwaha to be identified as author of this work has been asserted by him in accordance with the Copyright, Designs and Patents Act 1988.

First published 2018

21 20 19
10 9 8 7 6 5 4 3

British Library Cataloguing in Publication Data
A catalogue record for this book is available from the British Library

ISBN 978 1 292 19161 4

Printed in Slovakia by Neografia

Pearson acknowledges use of the following extracts
P2: Time series: RPI: Ave price Bread: white loaf, sliced, 800g, Office for National Statistics, Contains public sector information licensed under the Open Government Licence v3.0;
P20: UK Property Transaction Statistics, HM Revenue & Customs, © 2018, Crown copyright, Contains public sector information licensed under the Open Government Licence v3.0;
P20: Office for Budget Responsibility: Economic and fiscal outlook, November 2016 © 2016, Crown copyright, Contains public sector information licensed under the Open Government Licence v3.0;
P90: Time series: RPI All item index: Jan 1987=100, Office for National Statistics, Crown copyright, Contains public sector information licensed under the Open Government Licence v3.0;
P90: Office for National Statistics, Crown copyright, Contains public sector information licensed under the Open Government Licence v3.0;
P91: Gross Domestic product: Quarter on Quarter growth: CVM SA%, Office for National Statistics, Crown copyright, Contains public sector information licensed under the Open Government Licence v3.0.

Notes from the publisher

1. While the publishers have made every attempt to ensure that advice on the qualification and its assessment is accurate, the official specification and associated assessment guidance materials are the only authoritative source of information and should always be referred to for definitive guidance.

   Pearson examiners have not contributed to any sections in this resource relevant to examination papers for which they have responsibility.

2. Pearson has robust editorial processes, including answer and fact checks, to ensure the accuracy of the content in this publication, and every effort is made to ensure this publication is free of errors. We are, however, only human, and occasionally errors do occur. Pearson is not liable for any misunderstandings that arise as a result of errors in this publication, but it is our priority to ensure that the content is accurate. If you spot an error, please do contact us at resourcescorrections@pearson.com so we can make sure it is corrected.

Contents

1-to-1
page match with the
GCSE Statistics
Revision Guide
ISBN 9781292191621

iii

A small bit of small print

Edexcel publishes Sample Assessment Material and the Specification on its website. This is the official content and this book should be used in conjunction with it. The questions have been written to help you practise every topic in the book.

Describing data

tier F **Guided**

1 Complete the sentences below using one of the following words:

discrete   continuous   categorical

The weight of a cat is ......<u>continuous</u>...... data.

The number of potatoes in a bag is <u>discrete</u>......... data.

The colour of a person's eyes is ......<u>cato</u>............. data.   **(2 marks)**

tier F **Guided**

2 Sandeep recorded the temperature, in °C, of the water on the surface of a lake at 9 am on each of 7 days. Here are his results.

10.1   7.3   9.2   6.3   5.1   8.4   7.2

Is temperature an example of continuous or discrete data?

Give a reason for your answer.

Continuous data because ......<u>Temprature canbe measured at any temp</u>......   **(2 marks)**

tier F

3 Ethan found the weight, in grams, of each of 50 cranberries. Circle the words from the list below that best describe the data he found.

> You can choose more than one word.

(2 marks)

(quantitative)   qualitative   discrete

(continuous)   ordinal   categorical

tier F

4 Here is a list of statistical words:

discrete   continuous   bivariate   ordinal   categorical

Choose the word from the list that best describes the data below.

(a) Number of orange juice cartons on a shelf

......<u>discrete</u>......   **(1 mark)**

(b) Length of a football pitch

......<u>Continuoy</u>......   **(1 mark)**

(c) Price and age of second-hand vans

......<u>bivariated</u>......   **(1 mark)**

(d) Position in a car race

......<u>ordinal</u>......   **(1 mark)**

tier H

5 Alison is planning to buy a new car. She knows the colour of car and the engine size she wants. Suggest a data item to complete a set of three multivariate data she might consider when choosing her new car.

......<u>model gj-he car</u>......

......   **(2 marks)**

Primary and secondary data

1 Kate wants to investigate how the price of a loaf of bread has changed from 2012 to 2017. She finds this information in a table on a government website.

Year	2012	2013	2014	2015	2016	2017
Price (p)	124	130	116	104	100	103

Source: Office for National Statistics

Explain whether this is primary or secondary data.

Secondary data because ....the data is collected by the office for.... ....national statistics....

(1 mark)

2 John wants to investigate whether the boys at his school watch more television than the girls at his school. He wants to collect primary data for his investigation. Describe the difference between primary data and secondary data.

....Primary data is collected by the person conducting the investigation.... ....whereby secondary data is collected by a third party....

(2 marks)

3 Jodie collected data from the internet on the heights of European men and the heights of African men.

(a) State **two** possible problems with obtaining data from the internet.

....Poor reliability and data could be not up to date....

(2 marks)

(b) Suggest **one** possible problem with collecting primary data in this situation.

....He may not have access to enough african or european men....

(2 marks)

4 A human resources manager is investigating how much time employees at a large company take off due to sickness. The human resources manager plans to collect primary data.
Give a reason why she should do this.

....There will be no relevant secondary data....

(2 marks)

5 Ravina is investigating whether adults are taller now than they were 100 years ago. Should Ravina use primary or secondary data? Give a reason for your answer.

....She should use secondary data as you cannot collect.... ....how you old death....

(2 marks)

Collecting data 1

Guided

1 Children at a nursery wear shirts of different colours. The colours of the shirts are red, black, white, blue and yellow. Tom is going to count the number of shirts of each colour.
Draw a table Tom could use to record the data he collects.

> Draw a table with three columns with the colours written in the first column.

(3 marks)

Colour	tally	total
Red		
Black		
white		
blue		
yellow		

2 Andrew is going to do a survey to find out the type of vegetable people like best.
Design a suitable data collection sheet for Andrew to use.

(2 marks)

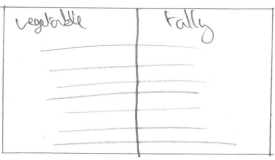

vegetable	tally

3 Here are the numbers of goals scored by a football team in each match last season.

1	4	3	2	2	2	3	4	1	2
3	4	1	2	3	3	4	1	4	3

Use a data collection sheet to record this information.

(3 marks)

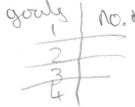

goals	No. of times scored goals
1	
2	
3	
4	

Guided

4 Jenny asks 50 car owners:

'How old is your car?'

Design a data collection sheet for Jenny to record this information.

> In this type of question the ages should be written as intervals. Make sure the intervals do not overlap.

(2 marks)

Age of car (in years)		
0 to less than 2		
2 to less than 4		

3

Collecting data 2

1 A scientist wants to investigate whether a new type of fertiliser helps tomatoes to grow bigger. He plans to run an experiment in a laboratory with tomato plants by growing them in the new fertiliser.

> Guided

   (a) Identify the explanatory and response variables in this experiment.

> The explanatory variable is the variable that is going to be investigated.

> The response variable is the variable that is the outcome.

Explanatory   Fertiliser

Response .... **(2 marks)**

   (b) Describe **one** advantage and **one** disadvantage of doing this as a laboratory experiment.

Advantage

....

Disadvantage

.... **(2 marks)**

2 A drugs company has invented a new drug that cures acne. The drugs company plans to run an experiment in a hospital with patients who suffer from acne.

   (a) Identify the explanatory and response variables in this experiment.

Explanatory ....

Response .... **(2 marks)**

Here is a list of statistical words:

     field   laboratory   natural

   (b) Use one of these words to complete the statement below.

     'The company's investigation is a .... experiment.' **(1 mark)**

   (c) Identify **one** possible extraneous variable.

.... **(1 mark)**

3 Isaac wants to find out if dogs are more active in the presence of children. He is going to carry out a laboratory experiment where dog owners record the activity of their dogs with and without children.
Discuss why laboratory results are more reliable.

....

....

.... **(2 marks)**

Collecting data 3

1 An advert for a brand of weedkiller states the following:

'Kills all weeds growing on your lawn.'

Callum wants to test this claim on his lawn.

(a) Identify the explanatory and response variables in this experiment.

Explanatory   *Weedkiller*

Response ....   **(2 marks)**

Here is a list of statistical words:

field   laboratory   natural

(b) Use one of these words to complete the statement below.

'Callum's investigation is a .... experiment.'   **(1 mark)**

(c) Give **one** advantage and **one** disadvantage of doing this type of experiment.

Advantage

....

Disadvantage

....   **(2 marks)**

(d) Identify **one** possible extraneous variable.

....   **(1 mark)**

2 Alex wants to investigate the average winter temperature in some cities.
He thinks this will be affected by the altitude of the city above sea level.
He states the following:

'For cities in the same country, the higher the altitude of the city above sea level the lower the winter temperature is.'

(a) Write down

(i) the explanatory variable

....

(ii) the response variable.

....

....   **(2 marks)**

(b) Identify **one** possible extraneous variable.

....

....   **(2 marks)**

Problems with collected data

1   Pierre is going to investigate whether there is a difference in the time spent on reading by boys and by girls during one week at his school.
He writes the following hypothesis for the investigation:

'Girls spend more time reading than boys do in one week.'

Pierre decides to use a census of the 1400 students at his school.
He is going to ask each student to record the time spent, to the nearest minute, on reading during one week.
Pierre collects this information on an online database.

Data record	Gender	Time spent on reading (nearest minute)
1	Male	52
2	Female	44
3	Girl	104
4	Boy	Ninety-one
5	M	24
6	F	41
7	Male	0
8	F	Sixty-one
9	Boy	7
10	G	

(a) Give **two** reasons why Pierre must clean the data before he uses it.

> Data must have consistent units, and all records must be complete.

....

.... **(2 marks)**

(b) Describe **two** ways of improving Pierre's data.

....

.... **(2 marks)**

Row 10 has data missing.

(c) What might this mean?

.... **(1 mark)**

(d) Discuss **two** ways in which Pierre's data collection plan could affect the reliability of his conclusions.

....

....

.... **(2 marks)**

Populations

1 There are 30 boys in a football squad. The manager needs to find out which exercises the boys want to do at their next training session.
He is going to ask all 30 boys.

Guided

(a) Write down the population.

> Remember to include the word 'all'.

All the 30 boys   **(1 mark)**

(b) Write down the statistical name for an investigation that gets information from every member of the population.

.... **(1 mark)**

(c) Give **one** reason why using a sample of the football squad is not necessary.

.... **(1 mark)**

2 Helena and Nina own a delivery service. They deliver parcels to 40 offices every day. Helena wants to use a census to collect each of the office managers' opinions.

(a) Write down **one** advantage of using a census.

.... **(1 mark)**

Nina wants to use a sample of the office managers rather than a census.

(b) Give **two** reasons why a sample might be better.

....

....

....

.... **(2 marks)**

3 Alex wants to investigate the numbers of hours spent on homework by all the children at his school last week.
Describe a suitable sampling frame that could be used.

....

.... **(1 mark)**

4 John wants to find information about the numbers of people travelling in cars in his town.
He is going to take a sample of the cars passing his house one Monday morning.
Explain why John's sample may be biased.

....

.... **(1 mark)**

Grouping data

1 Here are the weights, to the nearest kilogram, of 30 girls.

70	52	61	63	52	62	60	63	58	65
56	67	56	67	68	66	58	59	37	40
68	69	53	59	62	64	45	63	54	64

Suggest suitable class intervals for this data.

$30 < x \leqslant 40$ .... $40 < x \leqslant 50$ .... x .... x ....   **(2 marks)**

2 Alan records the amount of rainfall, in cm, that falls each day in his village in December.

Here are the results.

2.3	1.5	0.4	1.8	3.5	4.3	1.0	3.0
5.5	4.2	2.2	0	0.9	5.4	3.2	2.7
3.7	2.5	1.9	0.3	0	3.6	0	3.2
2.6	1.3	2.2	1.2	5.8	5.1	3.6	

Suggest suitable class intervals for this data.

> Try not to have too many or too few intervals.

....

....

....   **(2 marks)**

3 Andrew is measuring the diameter, in mm, of some metal ropes.
Here are the results.

62.81	70.34	80.43	62.35	63.82	81.61	73.24	83.99	52.35	86.41
88.23	74.43	73.86	64.16	66.43	62.73	58.67	75.38	76.26	85.83
75.94	53.97	78.53	67.77	51.39	69.35	57.85	78.74	72.91	70.85

(a) Suggest suitable class intervals for this data.

....

....

....   **(2 marks)**

Andrew measured the diameter of another metal rope.
The diameter of the metal rope was 120.35 mm.

(b) Suggest a new interval to allow for this metal rope.

....

....   **(1 mark)**

Random sampling

1 Explain what is meant by a random sample.

> You must give a clear explanation by using **key** words.

....

.... **(1 mark)**

2 There are 180 girls in Year 11 in a school. Seven of these girls are going to represent the school at a charity event. The headteacher decides to use simple random sampling to select the seven girls.
Describe how the headteacher could do this.

> You must give **three** points in your answer as this question is worth **three** marks. The first point is done for you.

1 Number all the girls from 0 to 179.

2 ....

3 .... **(3 marks)**

3 A human resources manager wants to find out what the workers think about the company pension scheme. She plans to use a survey of workers in the company. She decides to use a random sample survey.

(a) Explain what is meant by the word 'random'.

....

.... **(1 mark)**

There are 1200 workers in the company.
The manager uses a computer to generate the following list of random numbers:

452   879   003   079   178   984   213   567   821   084

(b) Explain how she can use these numbers to select the 10 workers in the sample.

....

....

.... **(3 marks)**

(c) Comment on the reliability of her sample.

....

.... **(1 mark)**

4 A headmaster wants to investigate how many students in the school are vegetarians. There are 1500 students in the school. He takes a sample of 50 of these students so that each of the 1500 students has the same chance of being selected.
Write down the statistical name for this type of sample.

....

.... **(1 mark)**

Stratified sampling 1

1 A council wants to open an Advice Centre in the city. They want to find out where the residents of the city want the centre to be located. The city is divided into 15 districts. The council will choose between two sampling methods.

Method 1	Method 2
Randomly select residents from each district in proportion to the number of residents in that district.	Select all the residents from three randomly selected districts.
Name of sampling method	
....	....

(a) Write down the name of each sampling method in the boxes above. **(2 marks)**

(b) Give **two** advantages of using Method 1 rather than Method 2.

....

....

.... **(2 marks)**

2 The table gives information about the ages of the members of a golf club.

Age (years)	16–29	30–39	40–54	55 and over
Number of members	46	63	81	78

The manager is going to take a sample of 40 of these people, stratified by age. Work out the number of people aged 40–54 years in the sample.

....

....

.... **(2 marks)**

3 A swimming club has members who specialise in only one swimming stroke. The table gives information about the number of members who specialise in each of the swimming strokes.

> Guided

Swimming stroke	Freestyle	Backstroke	Breaststroke	Butterfly
Number of members	105	70	110	65

The club coach wants to take a sample of 40 members.
Work out the number of swimmers for each stroke in the sample.

> The sample must have the same relative proportions for each stroke as in the whole club.

> There must be a whole number of swimmers for each stroke.

Total number of members = 105 + 70 + ... + ... = ...

Freestyle: $\frac{105}{350} \times 40$ = ...   Backstroke: $\frac{.........}{350} \times$ .... = ...

Breaststroke: $\frac{.........}{.........} \times$ .... = ..., rounded .... to ....

Butterfly: $\frac{.........}{.........} \times$ .... = ..., rounded .... to ....   **(4 marks)**

Non-random sampling

1 A company makes bolts. On Monday the company makes 9000 bolts. A systematic sample of 1% of the total number of bolts is going to be taken for testing.

> **Guided**

(a) Describe in detail how this sample should be selected.

> 1% means choosing one item out of every 100.

Sample every ....th bolt

Start at .... **(2 marks)**

(b) Give **one** disadvantage of using this sampling method.

....

.... **(1 mark)**

2 There are 43 police forces in England and Wales. The Police Federation wants to find out the opinions of police officers on a planned change to working hours. They decide to choose five forces at random and survey all the police officers in these forces.

(a) State **one** advantage and **one** disadvantage of using this sampling method.

Advantage

....

Disadvantage

.... **(2 marks)**

(b) Write down the name of this sampling method.

....

.... **(1 mark)**

3 Maria is carrying out an investigation into the amount of time spent by adults reading newspapers. She is going to ask 100 adults some questions. She asks adults going to a library until she has asked 50 men and 50 women.

(a) Write down the name of this sampling method.

....

.... **(1 mark)**

(b) Give **one** advantage and **one** disadvantage of this sampling method.

Advantage

....

Disadvantage

.... **(2 marks)**

Stratified sampling 2

Guided

1 The table shows information about the numbers of people who attended a local charity event.

	Age		
	Under 18	**18–50**	**Over 50**
Male	84	64	95
Female	48	32	77

Sandeep carries out a survey of a sample of the people, stratified by age and gender. There are 8 people who are male and between the ages 18–50 in his sample.
Work out the number of people who are female and under 18 in his sample.

> Work out the total number of people first and then calculate the sample size. The sample size must be smaller than the total number.

Total number of people = 84 + 64 + ... + ... + ... + ... = ...

$$\frac{64}{total} = \frac{8}{sample\ size}$$

Sample size = $8 \times \frac{........}{64}$ = ...

Number of females under 18 = $\frac{48}{........} \times ....$ = ...

(3 marks)

2 The table gives information about the numbers of students studying languages at a college.

	Language studied			
	French	**Spanish**	**Italian**	**Total**
Boys	17	33	24	74
Girls	24	13	29	66
Total	41	46	53	140

Ravina is going to take a sample of 30 students, stratified by gender and language studied. Work out the number of boys studying Spanish in her sample.

....

.... **(2 marks)**

3 The table shows information about the activities students choose when they go on an outdoors pursuits programme.

	Climbing	**Sailing**	**Canoeing**
Male	18	35	26
Female	16	42	21

The coach gives a questionnaire to some of the students.
He takes a sample of 30 students, stratified by gender and the activity chosen.
Work out the number of female students who chose canoeing he should have in his sample.

....

.... **(2 marks)**

Petersen capture-recapture formula

1 Jim has a box containing a large number of counters. He wants to find an estimate for the number of counters in the box. Jim takes a sample of 60 counters from the box. He marks each counter with a pen. He then puts the counters back in the box. Jim shakes the box.

He now takes another sample of 50 counters from the box.

6 of these counters have been marked with a pen.

Work out an estimate for the total number of counters in the box.

> Let n be the total population. n must be bigger than the size of the sample.

$$\frac{60}{n} = \frac{6}{50} \text{ so } n = \frac{60 \times 50}{6} = \text{.........}$$

(2 marks)

2 Andrew wants to find an estimate for the number of ants in a colony in the ground.
He catches 70 ants from the colony and marks each one with some paint.
He then returns the ants to the colony.
The next day Andrew catches another 80 ants from the colony.
12 of these ants are marked with the paint.

(a) Work out an estimate for the number of ants in the colony.

> You cannot have fractions of ants, so give your answer as a whole number, rounding up or down as necessary.

....

....

.... **(2 marks)**

(b) Write down any assumptions you have made.

....

.... **(1 mark)**

3 Nancy wants to estimate the number of frogs in a lake. She catches a sample of 12 frogs, marks them with some dye and puts them back in the lake.
Later that day, in a second sample of 12 frogs, she finds that 2 of them are marked with the dye.

(a) Work out an estimate for the number of frogs in the lake.

....

....

.... **(2 marks)**

(b) How reliable is Nancy's estimate?
Give reasons for your answer.

....

....

.... **(2 marks)**

Controlling extraneous variables 1

1   Asha conducted an experiment to investigate the number of calories used by people exercising for different periods of time on a treadmill in the gym.
Asha recorded the number of calories used, in kcal, and the length of time, in minutes, for each person.

(a)   What is the explanatory variable in this experiment?

> The explanatory variable is the variable that is going to be investigated.

....

.... **(1 mark)**

(b)   What is the response variable in this experiment?

> The response variable is the variable that is the outcome.

....

.... **(1 mark)**

(c)   Identify an extraneous variable in this experiment and describe how this could be controlled.

> An extraneous variable is a variable that you are not interested in but that could affect the result of the experiment.

....

.... **(2 marks)**

2   Beverley is carrying out a laboratory experiment to test whether listening to music affects a student's ability to learn multiplication tables.
She is going to give the students 20 questions each and then test each student to see how many questions they can answer correctly.
Beverley is going to repeat the same experiment with all the students listening to music.

(a)   What is the explanatory variable in this experiment?

....

.... **(1 mark)**

(b)   What is the response variable in this experiment?

.... **(1 mark)**

(c)   Identify **two** extraneous variables in this experiment and describe how they can be controlled.

1   ....

2   .... **(2 marks)**

3   A researcher wanted to find out if lack of sleep causes more driving errors.
He selected two groups of ten people. Each person in the first group was only allowed 2 hours of sleep. Each person in the second group was allowed 7 hours of sleep.
Both groups sat a Hazard Perception test at a driving centre at 10 am the next morning.
Identify **two** extraneous variables in this experiment and describe how they can be controlled.

1   ....

2   .... **(2 marks)**

Controlling extraneous variables 2

1 Some people think that drinking tea before bedtime may help to increase the number of hours of deep sleep. David wants to research this.
Explain why David might use a control group.

....

.... **(1 mark)**

2 A scientist is going to do an experiment on some patients to find out if using a new drug will cure a disease.
The scientist should use a control group.

> The control group will test the effectiveness of the drug.

(a) Explain why.

The control group is used to compare the patients who take the new drug with

.... **(1 mark)**

(b) Describe how the scientist would do this.

....

....

.... **(2 marks)**

3 Tanya wants to investigate if children learn the alphabet better with diagrams. She plans an experiment for her class. She matches the 20 children in her class in pairs.
One child in each pair learns the alphabet using diagrams. The other child in the pair learns the alphabet without using diagrams. After one month, she gives all of the class a test.

(a) Describe how Tanya could match the children in pairs.

> Think about similarities among all the children in the same class.

....

.... **(1 mark)**

(b) Describe a method that Tanya could use to decide which child in each pair should learn the alphabet using diagrams.

....

.... **(1 mark)**

(c) Matched pair experiments help to reduce the effect of which type of variable?

....

.... **(1 mark)**

Questionnaires and interviews 1

tier F&H

1 Billy wants to find out how many times people go to the local shop.
He asks this question on a questionnaire:

> How many times do you go to the local shop?
>
> 1–3   3–6   6–9   9 or more
> ☐   ☐   ☐   ☐

Write down **two** things that are wrong with this question.

> You need to ask yourself: Is there a time frame? Are the response boxes overlapping? Are the response boxes exhaustive?

....

.... **(2 marks)**

tier F&H

2 A town council wants information about local people's use of the leisure centre.
Two methods of collecting information have been suggested:

> Method 1: Ask people at a local supermarket about their use of the leisure centre.
>
> Method 2: Send a questionnaire to all council tax payers.

Which method is likely to give the more reliable results?
Give **one** reason for your answer.

....

.... **(2 marks)**

tier F&H

3 Rebecca designs a questionnaire to give to customers in her coffee shop.
One question on Rebecca's questionnaire is:

> 'Do you agree that the cakes are good value for money?'

This is **not** a good question.

(a) Give **one** reason why.

....

.... **(1 mark)**

Rebecca wants to use face-to-face interviews with the customers in her coffee shop.

(b) Give **one** advantage and **one** disadvantage of using face-to-face interviews rather than a questionnaire given to customers.

Advantage

....

Disadvantage

.... **(2 marks)**

tier F&H

4 Anna wants to find out how far students live from her school.
She uses this question on a questionnaire:

> How far do you live from school?
> very near   near   far   very far

Write down **two** things that are wrong with this question.

....

.... **(2 marks)**

Questionnaires and interviews 2

1 A publishing company wants to estimate the proportion of people who photocopied pages from textbooks illegally last month.
They want people to be able to give answers so they designed the survey below.

> Flip a fair coin. Keep the result to yourself.
> • If you get heads on the coin, ignore the question and tick box **A**.
> • If you get tails on the coin, answer the question.
> Have you photocopied pages from any textbook illegally during the last month?
>
> | If yes, tick box **A** | If no, tick box **B** |
> |:---:|:---:|
> | ☐ | ☐ |
> | **A** | **B** |

This method, of deciding whether or not to answer a question by spinning a coin, is called the random response technique.

(a) Explain why this method is used.

....

....

.... **(1 mark)**

500 people completed the survey.

(b) Estimate the number of people who got heads on the coin.

$\dfrac{1}{\text{.......}} \times 500 = $ .... **(1 mark)**

270 of the 500 people ticked box A.

(c) Estimate the proportion of people who photocopied pages from textbooks illegally during the last month.

Estimate for the number who ticked box A who were truthful

= .... − .... = ...

Estimate for the proportion of people who photocopied pages from textbooks

illegally

$= \dfrac{\text{............}}{500 - \text{............}} = \dfrac{\text{............}}{\text{............}} = \dfrac{\text{.......}}{\text{.......}} = $ .... = ...% **(2 marks)**

Hypotheses

1 Alan wants to investigate the pressure of gas in gas bottles used for barbecues.
He thinks this will be affected by the age of the gas bottles.
He writes down two statements:

     Statement A: Do older gas bottles have lower pressure?

     Statement B: The older the gas bottle the lower the gas pressure.

Statement A is **not** a hypothesis.

(a) Explain why.

> A hypothesis must be specific and measurable.

....

.... **(1 mark)**

Alan uses Statement B as his hypothesis.

(b) Write down **two** variables Alan needs to include in his investigation.

Variable 1 ....

Variable 2 .... **(2 marks)**

2 Sam lives near an airport. He wants to investigate how the distance from the airport affects house prices in the area around the airport.

(a) Write down a hypothesis he could use.

....

.... **(1 mark)**

(b) Describe how he could collect secondary data to test his hypothesis.

....

.... **(1 mark)**

3 A researcher is going to investigate the age at which people in Scotland get asthma. He wants to find out if men get asthma at a younger age than women.

(a) Write down a hypothesis that the researcher could use.

....

.... **(1 mark)**

It would be difficult for a researcher to use a census.

(b) Write down a reason why.

....

.... **(1 mark)**

Designing investigations

Guided

1 A council wants to find out what people think of a new cinema. The council sends out a pilot survey to 350 people and gets 250 completed surveys back.
The council wants to get at least 600 completed surveys.

(a) How many people should the council send the full survey to?

> Let n = the number of people the survey is sent to. n must be bigger than 600, which is the total number of completed surveys the council wants.

$$\frac{250}{350} = \frac{600}{n}, \text{ so } n = \frac{600 \times 350}{250} = \ldots\ldots\ldots\ldots$$

(2 marks)

The council decides to collect information using a questionnaire.

(b) State **one** advantage and **one** disadvantage of using a questionnaire rather than face-to-face interviews.

Advantage

....

Disadvantage

.... **(2 marks)**

The following question is used in the council's questionnaire:

'Do you agree that the new cinema was a good use of local taxpayers' money?'

This is **not** a good question.

(c) Give **two** reasons why.

1 ....

....

2 ....

.... **(2 marks)**

2 Richard is the manager of a large chain of hotels. He wants to investigate the differences between the numbers of sick days taken by employees in different age groups.
He obtains the following information about the ages of the employees.

Age group	Number of male employees	Number of female employees
18–30	72	43
31–50	82	56
51–65	36	43

Assess the suitability of taking a sample of 15 employees stratified by age and by gender, for his investigation

....

....

....

.... **(3 marks)**

Tables

1   The table shows information about the numbers of house and flat sales with values of £40 000 or more for the years 2015 to 2017.
All figures have been rounded to the nearest ten.

Year	England	Scotland	Wales	Northern Ireland	UK
2015	1 054 370	100 320	51 010	23 880	1 229 580
2016	1 057 820	99 450	53 150	24 600	1 235 020
2017	1 032 610	104 450	56 280	26 390	1 219 730

Source: HM Revenue and Customs

(a) Write down the number of house and flat sales in Northern Ireland in the year 2016.

> Find the 2016 row and the Northern Ireland column.

.... **(1 mark)**

(b) Work out the difference between the highest number and the lowest number of house and flat sales per year in England.

> Find the highest and lowest numbers in the England column.

....

.... **(2 marks)**

(c) Describe the trend in the number of house and flat sales in Wales for the years 2015 to 2017.

> A trend can be described as upwards, downwards or level.

.... **(1 mark)**

2   The table shows the Gross Domestic Product (GDP) and the population of the United Kingdom for the years 2016 to 2019.

Year	UK GDP (£ billion)	UK population (million)	GDP per capita (£000s)	
2016	1885.5	64.768	29 112	actual
2017	1962.9	65.200	30 106	actual
2018	2029.5	65.635	30 921	estimate
2019	2094.8	65.073	32 192	estimate

Source: budgetresponsibility.org.uk

> GDP per capita is the GDP per person in the country.

(a) Write down the year in which the GDP per capita is the lowest.

.... **(1 mark)**

(b) Write down the year in which the data shows a fall in the population of the UK.

.... **(1 mark)**

(c) Describe the trend in the GDP of the UK.

.... **(1 mark)**

Two-way tables

1 The two-way table shows some information about the numbers of students in a school.

	Year group			Total
	Year 7	**Year 9**	**Year 11**	
Boys		126	115	456
Girls		132		433
Total	315	258		889

Complete the two-way table.

Total girls = 889 − 456 = 433   Year 9 boys = 258 − 132 = 126

Year 7 boys = 456 − .... − .... = ...   Year 7 girls = 315 − .... = ...

Year 11 total = 889 − 315 − 258 = ...   Year 11 girls = ... − 115 = ...   **(3 marks)**

2 The two-way table gives some information about the types of sandwich filling 100 children had on one day.

	Type of filling			Total
	Ham	**Cheese**	**Tuna**	
Boys	10		14	43
Girls	22			
Total	32	30		100

(a) Complete the two-way table.   **(3 marks)**

(b) How many children had a ham filling?

.... **(1 mark)**

(c) How many boys had a filling of any kind?

.... **(1 mark)**

3 Rachael asks 100 students if they like mathematics, physics or French best.
39 of the students are girls. 23 of these girls like mathematics best.
17 boys like French best. 6 out of the 22 students who like physics best are girls.
Work out the number of students who like mathematics best.

> Draw a two-way table. Always write down the given numbers in the table.

(3 marks)

Pictograms

1 The pictogram gives information about the numbers of cars sold in the last 4 months.

Month	Number of cars sold
April	▭ ▭ ▭
May	▭ ▭ ▭ ▭
June	▭ ▭ ▭
July	▭ ▭
August	

Key: ▭ represents 8 cars

(a) Write down the number of cars sold in June.

> Quarter of the large rectangle represents 2 cars.

8 + 8 + 2 = ... cars

(2 marks)

In August, 36 cars were sold.

(b) Show this information in the pictogram.

> Divide 36 by 8 to find the number of large rectangles and the fraction left over.

(1 mark)

Sandeep thinks the total number of cars sold in the months April to August inclusive is 130.

(c) Is he correct? Give a reason for your answer.

....

.... **(2 marks)**

2 The pictogram gives information about the numbers of flower bouquets sold in the last 4 days.

Day	Number of bouquets sold
Monday	▭ ▭
Tuesday	▭ ▭ ▭
Wednesday	▭ ▭
Thursday	▭ ▭
Friday	

Key: ▭ represents .... bouquets

On Tuesday, 12 bouquets were sold.

(a) Complete the key. **(2 marks)**

(b) Write down the number of bouquets sold on Thursday.

....

.... **(1 mark)**

On Friday, 17 bouquets were sold.

(c) Show this information in the pictogram. **(1 mark)**

Bar charts 1

1 In a survey people were asked to say which of five European cities they planned to visit next year.

The table shows the percentage of the people surveyed who said that city.

City	Percentage
Athens	20
Berlin	25
Madrid	10
Paris	30
Rome	15

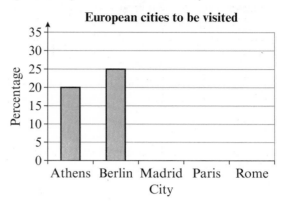

(a) Complete the bar chart to show this information. **(2 marks)**

(b) Write down the name of the city which had the **second highest** percentage.

> Identify the second tallest bar on the bar chart.

.... **(1 mark)**

(c) Which city was the least popular?

> Identify the smallest bar on the bar chart.

.... **(1 mark)**

2 Mark asked some adults to choose a favourite colour. Here are his results.

Favourite colour	Red	Yellow	Blue	Pink	Grey
Frequency	36	42	12	18	28

The incomplete bar chart shows this information.

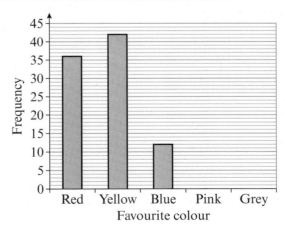

(a) Complete the bar chart for the missing colours. **(2 marks)**

(b) Write down the colour which was chosen the most often.

.... **(1 mark)**

(c) Write down the colour which was chosen by half as many adults as chose red.

.... **(1 mark)**

Bar charts 2

1 The multiple bar chart shows some information about the shoe sizes of the men and women who work at a supermarket.

The data for shoe size 7 has not been included. The data for shoe size 7 is:

Men: 29; Women: 48.

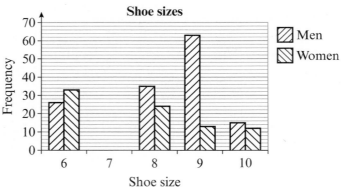

(a) Complete the multiple bar chart.   **(2 marks)**

(b) Write down the number of men with a shoe size 8.

....   **(1 mark)**

(c) Write down the most common shoe size for the women.

....   **(1 mark)**

(d) Compare the number of men with shoe size 9 with the number of women with shoe size 9.

....

....   **(2 marks)**

2 The table shows some information about the number of months, n, some children have owned a laptop.

Number of months	$n < 4$	$4 \leqslant n < 8$	$8 \leqslant n < 16$	$16 \leqslant n < 30$	$30 \leqslant n < 40$	$n \geqslant 40$
Boys %	34	18	14	15	6	13
Girls %	42	20	19	9	4	6

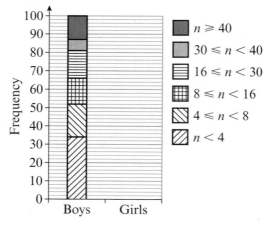

(a) Use the information in the table to complete the composite bar chart.   **(3 marks)**

(b) Using information in the composite bar chart, what conclusions can you make about the number of months these children have owned a laptop?

> The number of marks given for the question indicates the number of conclusions you need to make.

....

....   **(2 marks)**

Stem and leaf diagrams

1 Anna is the secretary of her running club.
She recorded the number of miles run by each runner in one week.
Here are her results.

17	21	23	32	48	46	34	12
13	26	27	36	43	35	38	

Draw an ordered stem and leaf diagram for this information. **(3 marks)**

```
1 | 7  3
2 | 1
3 |
4 |
```

> Start with an unordered stem and leaf diagram.

```
1 | 2  3
2 | 1
3 |
4 |
```

> Now order the stem and leaf diagram.

> Always add a key to the finished diagram.

Key: .... | .... represents ....

2 Tom recorded the heart rate, in beats per minute, for each of 15 students before they ran.
Tom then asked the 15 students to run along the corridor.
He recorded their heart rates again.
Here are the results.

	Heart rate (beats per minute)														
Before running	71	62	82	78	55	68	60	74	77	66	80	61	72	58	68
After running	88	85	97	93	76	98	63	85	99	91	87	72	79	66	69

(a) Draw an ordered back-to-back stem and leaf diagram to represent this information.

(4 marks)

(b) Comment on the difference between the heart rates before running and the heart rates after running of the 15 students.

....

....

(2 marks)

Pie charts 1

1 Mark carried out a survey of some adults. He asked the adults what was their favourite type of film. The accurate pie chart shows some of this information.

> **Guided**

Use the pie chart to complete the table.

Favourite type of film

Type of film	Number of adults	Angle of sector
Horror	18	90°
Animation		65°
Science fiction	21	
Thriller		40°
Foreign		

> Use the Horror row to work out the number of degrees for 1 adult.

Horror: $\frac{90}{18}$ = ...° per adult

Animation: Number of adults = $\frac{65}{.......}$ = ...

Science fiction: Angle of sector = 21 × .... = ...

> Use the fact that the angles must add up to 360° to find the missing angle for Foreign films.

Thriller: Number of adults = $\frac{40}{.......}$ = ...

Foreign: Angle of sector = 360 − 90 − 65 − .... − 40 = ...

Foreign: Number of adults = $\frac{.......}{.......}$ = ...

(3 marks)

2 Giles has a farm with some animals. The accurate pie chart shows some information about the animals.

> **Guided**

(a) Write down the fraction of animals that are

   (i) goats

$\frac{.......}{360}$ = $\frac{.......}{4}$

   (ii) hens.

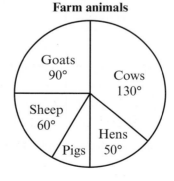

Farm animals

.... **(2 marks)**

There are 13 cows on the farm.

(b) How many pigs are on the farm?   > Work out the number of degrees for 1 animal.

....

.... **(2 marks)**

(c) How many animals are on the farm?   > Use your answer from part (b) to work out the total number of animals.

....

.... **(2 marks)**

Pie charts 2

Guided

1 Tom asked 60 students to name their favourite juice. Here are his results:

Juice	Apple	Carrot	Mango	Orange
Frequency	20	25	5	10
Angle	120°			

Draw an accurate pie chart for his results.

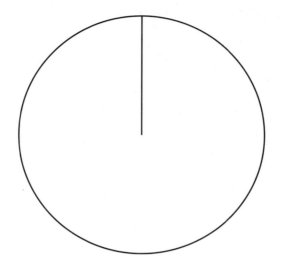

(3 marks)

Apple: $\frac{20}{60} \times 360 = 120°$ Carrot: $\frac{25}{60} \times 360 = ...$

Mango: $\frac{..........}{60} \times 360 = ...$ Orange: $\frac{..........}{..........} \times .... = ...$

> Make sure the angles add up to 360°.

2 The table shows information about 40 vehicles crossing a bridge.

Vehicle	Car	Lorry	Bus	Motorcycle
Frequency	9	11	6	14

Draw an accurate pie chart for these results.

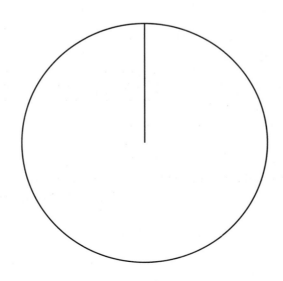

(3 marks)

Comparative pie charts

1 The comparative pie charts give information about the numbers of adults who had laser treatment for their eyes in 2005 and in 2015, and their ages.

Guided

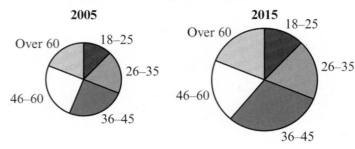

(a) Compare the total number of adults who had laser treatment in 2005 with the total number of adults who had laser treatment in 2015. Explain how you reached your conclusion.

Numbers have .... between 2005 and 2015. The .... of

the pie chart for 2015 is .... than the pie chart for 2005.   **(2 marks)**

(b) Describe how the number of people in the age group 46–60 who had laser treatment changed between 2005 and 2015.
Explain how you reached your conclusion.

....

.... **(2 marks)**

2 The table shows information about sales of mobile phones from different manufacturers in 2016 and 2017 in Mel's shop.

Guided

Make	Apple	Microsoft	LG	Samsung
Number sold in 2016	131	42	100	177
Number sold in 2017	216	172	179	315

Mel plans to draw comparative pie charts to show the information for each year.

(a) Find the size of the angle she should use for LG in the 2016 pie chart.

> Work out the total number of mobile phones sold in 2016.

Angle for LG in 2016 $= \dfrac{..........}{.........} \times .... = ...$ **(2 marks)**

Mel uses a radius of 5 cm for the 2016 pie chart.

(b) Work out the radius she should use for the 2017 pie chart.

> Work out the total numbersof mobile phones sold in 2017.

Total number of phones sold in 2017

$= 216 + 172 + ... + ... = ...$

$\dfrac{R^2}{r^2} = \dfrac{N}{n}$, so $R^2 = r^2 \times \dfrac{N}{n}$

$R^2 = 5^2 \times \dfrac{..........}{.........}$, so $R^2 = ..., R = \sqrt{.........} = ...$ cm   **(2 marks)**

Population pyramids

1 The two population pyramids show the percentages of men and women born in each age group in the United States and in Germany who were alive in 2000.

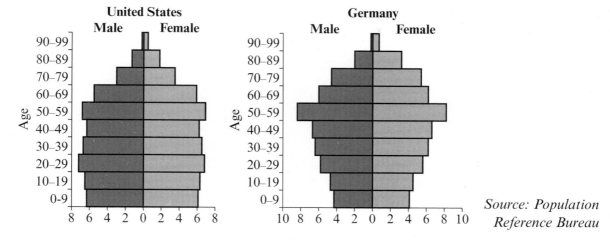

Source: Population Reference Bureau

(a) Write down the age group that has the greatest percentages of:

(i) males in the USA

> Find the age groups with the longest bars.

....

(ii) females in Germany

.... **(2 marks)**

In Germany, 2% of males and 3.2% of females are in the same age group.

(b) Write down this age group.

.... **(1 mark)**

2 The two population pyramids show the percentages of men and women in each age group in West Africa and Western Europe in 2015.

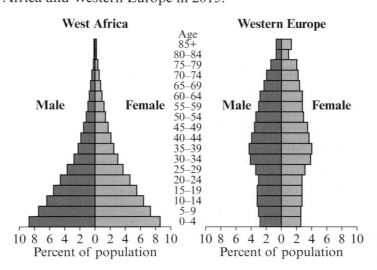

Source: Population Reference Bureau

Select an age range and compare the ages of men and women in West Africa and Western Europe in 2015.

....

.... **(2 marks)**

Choropleth maps

Guided

1 A piece of land is divided into 25 squares of equal size.
Andrew counts the number of rocks in each square.
His results are shown in the table.

5	5	6	7	7
6	6	7	7	9
7	7	7	8	9
8	9	9	11	13
9	11	13	14	15

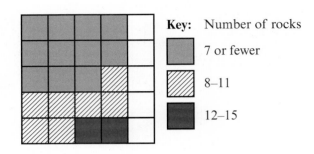

Key: Number of rocks

▨ 7 or fewer

▨ 8–11

▨ 12–15

20 squares on the choropleth map have already been shaded.

(a) Use the information in the table to complete the choropleth map. **(2 marks)**

(b) Describe how the rocks are spread across the land.

The number of rocks increases as ....

.... **(2 marks)**

Guided

2 Part of a beach is divided into 25 squares of equal size.
Andrew counts the number of sunbathers in each square.
His results are shown in the table.

7	8	8	10	10
5	5	6	7	7
3	3	4	4	5
1	1	2	3	3
1	1	2	2	2

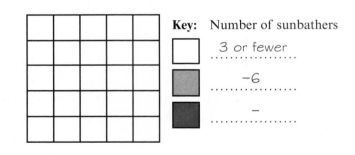

Key: Number of sunbathers

☐ 3 or fewer

▨ –6

▨ –

| 7 | represents seven sunbathers in the square.

(a) Use the information in the table to complete the choropleth map. **(2 marks)**

(b) Describe how the sunbathers are spread across the beach.

....

.... **(2 marks)**

Histograms and frequency polygons

1 The table gives information about house prices in a large village.

House prices, p (£00 000s)	$1 < p \leq 2$	$2 < p \leq 3$	$3 < p \leq 4$	$4 < p \leq 5$	$5 < p \leq 6$
Number of houses	3	6	7	9	5

(a) Draw a histogram to show the information in the table.   **(2 marks)**

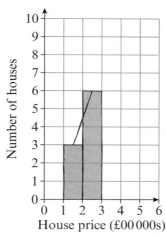

Draw the frequency polygon by joining the midpoints of the tops of the histogram bars with straight lines.

(b) Draw a frequency polygon for this data.   **(2 marks)**

(c) Write down the price class interval with the most houses.

....   **(1 mark)**

2 The table shows information about the weights of some football players.

Weight (w kg)	$70 < w \leq 80$	$80 < w \leq 90$	$90 < w \leq 100$	$100 < w \leq 110$	$110 < w \leq 120$
Frequency	6	9	12	9	7

(a) Draw a histogram to show the information in the table.

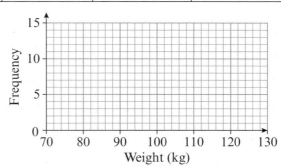

(b) Draw a frequency polygon for this data.   **(2 marks)**

(c) Write down the weight class interval with the highest frequency.

....   **(1 mark)**

(d) How many football players weigh more than 90 kg?

....

....   **(2 marks)**

Cumulative frequency diagrams 1

tier
F&H

Guided

1 The table shows information about the masses (w grams) of 80 oranges.

Weight (w g)	$80 < w \leqslant 90$	$90 < w \leqslant 100$	$100 < w \leqslant 110$	$110 < w \leqslant 120$	$120 < w \leqslant 130$
Frequency	6	14	17	29	14
Cumulative frequency	6	6 + 14 = 20	20 + 17 = ...	.... + ... = ...	.... + ... = ...

(a) Complete the cumulative frequency table. **(1 mark)**

(b) On the grid, draw a cumulative frequency graph. **(2 marks)**

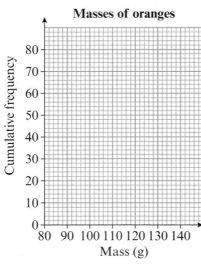

Masses of oranges

Plot the cumulative frequency at the top bound of each interval.

Draw a smooth curve, making sure it passes through each point on the graph.

tier
F&H

2 Adam records the distance, m miles, he drives each day for 100 days.
Some information about the results is given in the table.

Distance (m miles)	$0 < m \leqslant 10$	$10 < m \leqslant 20$	$20 < m \leqslant 30$	$30 < m \leqslant 40$	$40 < m \leqslant 50$	$50 < m \leqslant 60$
Frequency	3	15	20	36	20	6
Cumulative frequency						

(a) Complete the cumulative frequency table. **(1 mark)**

(b) On the grid, draw a cumulative frequency graph.

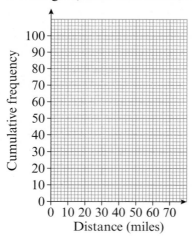

(2 marks)

Cumulative frequency diagrams 2

1 The cumulative frequency graph shows information about the speeds of 60 cars on a French motorway one Saturday afternoon.

(a) Find an estimate for the number of cars that have speeds less than 125 km/h.

.... **(1 mark)**

> Find 125 km/h on the horizontal axis and read up to the curved line and across to the vertical axis.

(b) Find an estimate for the number of cars that have speeds more than 130 km/h.

.... **(1 mark)**

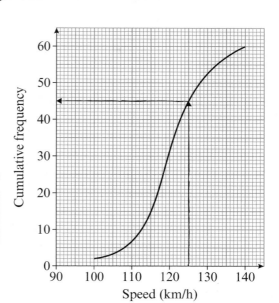

2 The table shows information about the ages of 90 members of a chess club.

Age (x years)	$5 < x \leq 15$	$15 < x \leq 25$	$25 < x \leq 35$	$35 < x \leq 45$	$45 < x \leq 55$
Frequency	11	28	23	19	9
Cumulative frequency					

> Work out the cumulative frequencies.

(a) On the grid, draw a cumulative frequency graph. **(2 marks)**

(b) Find an estimate for the number of members who are less than 20 years old.

> Find 20 years on the horizontal axis and go up to the curved line and read across on the vertical axis.

....

....

(1 mark)

(c) Find an estimate for the number of members who are more than 44 years old.

....

....

(1 mark)

The shape of a distribution

1 Mason and Daisy compared the lengths of time they each spent using their mobile phones on 11 days.
The table shows the times they each spent, in minutes.

Mason	22	24	42	35	34	24	41	50	37	20	25
Daisy	43	47	68	57	54	51	62	69	60	35	53

(a) Draw a back-to-back ordered stem and leaf diagram for the times they spent using their mobile phones each day. **(3 marks)**

```
     Mason              Daisy
 5 0 4 4 2 | 2 |
     7 4 5 | 3 |
       1 2 | 4 |
         0 | 5 |
           | 6 |
```

> Start with an unordered back-to-back stem and leaf diagram.

```
     Mason              Daisy
           | 2 |
           | 3 |
           | 4 |
           | 5 |
           | 6 |
```

> Order the back-to-back stem and leaf diagram.

> Make sure you give a key for the stem and leaf diagram.

Key: ....|........|........ represents ....

(b) Comment on the shapes of the distributions of Mason's and Daisy's phone use.

....

.... **(1 mark)**

2 The table gives information about the heights, in cm, of some plants.

Height, h (cm)	$20 < p \leqslant 30$	$30 < p \leqslant 40$	$40 < p \leqslant 50$	$50 < p \leqslant 60$	$60 < p \leqslant 70$
Frequency	3	5	10	15	12

(a) Draw a histogram to show the information in the table.

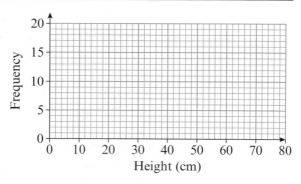

(2 marks)

(b) Draw a frequency polygon for this data. **(2 marks)**

(c) Comment on the shape of the distribution of the heights of the plants.

....

.... **(1 mark)**

Histograms with unequal class widths 1

1 The table shows information about the times, in minutes, that runners took to complete a race.

Time, t (minutes)	$0 < t \le 15$	$15 < t \le 45$	$45 < t \le 60$	$60 < t \le 70$	$70 < t \le 90$
Frequency	30	135	75	38	12
Class width	15	30	15	10	20
Frequency density	$\dfrac{30}{15} = 2$	$\dfrac{135}{30} = \dots$	$\dfrac{\dots}{\dots} = \dots$	$\dfrac{\dots}{\dots} = \dots$	$\dfrac{\dots}{\dots} = \dots$

> Add two extra rows to the table for your calculations.

> Frequency density = $\dfrac{\text{frequency}}{\text{class width}}$

On the grid, draw a histogram to show this information.

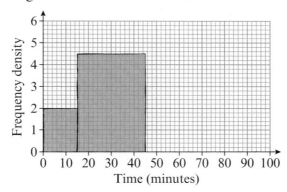

Time (minutes)

(3 marks)

2 The table shows information about the times, in minutes, that some shoppers spent in a clothes shop.

Time, t (minutes)	$15 < t \le 20$	$20 < t \le 30$	$30 < t \le 45$	$45 < t \le 55$	$55 < t \le 75$
Frequency	6	33	42	38	18

Draw a histogram to show this information.

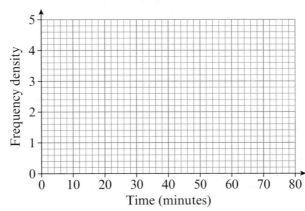

Time (minutes)

(3 marks)

Histograms with unequal class widths 2

1 The incomplete histogram and the incomplete table show information about the ages of people watching a play at a theatre.

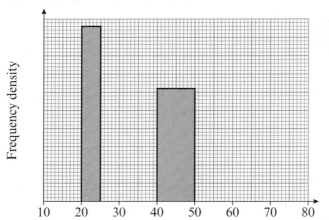

Age (*a* years)	Number of people
$10 \leqslant a < 20$	38
$20 \leqslant a < 25$	24
$25 \leqslant a < 40$	63
$40 \leqslant a < 50$	
$50 \leqslant a < 80$	24

(a) Use the histogram to complete the table.

Frequency density = $\dfrac{24}{5}$ = ...

> Find the frequency density of the class interval $20 \leqslant a < 25$ so that you can label the vertical axis.

Class width for $40 \leqslant a < 50$ = ...

Frequency density for $40 \leqslant a < 50$ = ...

> Use this to label the scale on the vertical axis.

Number of people in $40 \leqslant a < 50$ class = ... × .... = ...   **(2 marks)**

(b) Complete the histogram for the missing classes $10 \leqslant a < 20$, $25 \leqslant a < 40$ and $50 \leqslant a < 80$.   **(2 marks)**

(c) Estimate the number of people who are between the ages of 16 and 29.

Number of people in class $10 \leqslant a < 20$ aged 16 or over = $\dfrac{20 - 16}{10}$ × 38 = ...

Number of people in class $20 \leqslant a < 25$ = ...

Number of people in class $25 \leqslant a < 40$ aged 29 or under = $\dfrac{29 - 25}{15}$ × 63 = ...

Total number of people who are between the ages of 16 and 29

= .... + ... + ... = ...   **(3 marks)**

2

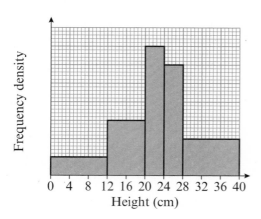

The histogram gives information about the heights of some vases. There are 60 vases with a height of 12 cm or less. Work out the fraction of the total number of vases which have a height of more than 32 cm.

....

....

....

....   **(4 marks)**

Misleading diagrams

1 The bar chart shows information about the breeds of dogs at a farm.

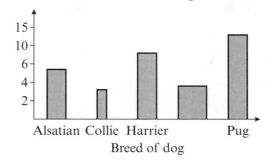

Write down **three** things that could be misleading or are wrong with the bar chart.

1 Missing label for one breed of dog

2 ....

3 .... **(2 marks)**

2 The diagram shows information about the sales of computers from a shop for each quarter of last year.

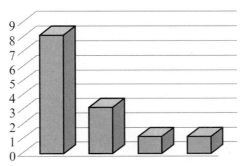

Write down **two** things that could be misleading in the diagram.

1 ....

2 .... **(2 marks)**

2 The graph gives information about the numbers of people using a butcher's shop in a village.

Write down **three** things that could be misleading or wrong with the graph.

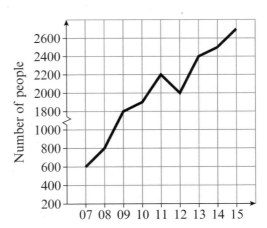

1 ....

2 ....

3 .... **(3 marks)**

37

Choosing the right format

1 The table shows some information about some children and the time they each took, to the nearest minute, to complete a puzzle on one afternoon.

Name	Avi	Ben	Debra	Sandeep	Rohan
Time (in minutes)	17	24	20	16	31

Explain whether or not it would be appropriate to represent the results of all of the children completing the puzzle using

(a) a time series graph

.... **(1 mark)**

(b) a histogram

.... **(1 mark)**

(c) a scatter diagram.

.... **(1 mark)**

2 The table below shows information about the numbers of cars at an auction on one Monday evening.

Make	Ford	Vauxhall	Nissan	Other
Frequency	10	18	14	24

John draws three different diagrams for this information.

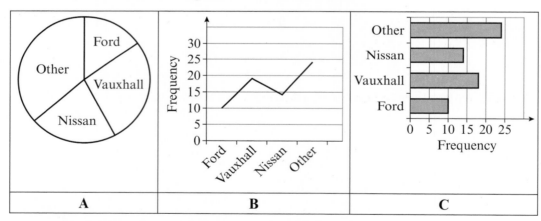

A	**B**	**C**

(a) Which diagram, **A** or **B** or **C**, is not appropriate for the data?
You must give a reason.

....

.... **(2 marks)**

John wants to show the proportions of cars to his teacher.

(b) Which diagram, **A** or **B** or **C**, is most appropriate for his data?
You must give a reason.

....

.... **(2 marks)**

Averages

1 Graham recorded the number of hours that he worked in the pizza shop each day last week.

   3   5   3   7   2   6   10

(a) Write down the mode.

> The mode is the number that occurs most often.

.... **(1 mark)**

(b) Work out the mean number of hours.

$$\text{Mean} = \frac{3 + 4 + 3 + \text{........} + \text{........} + \text{........} + \text{........}}{\text{........}} = \frac{\text{........}}{\text{........}} = \text{........ hours}$$

.... **(1 mark)**

(c) Find the median number of hours.

> Write the numbers of hours in order, from smallest to largest.

$$\text{Median} = \frac{7 + 1}{2}\text{th value} = \frac{8}{2} = \text{........th}$$

value, so choose the ....th value.

....

.... **(2 marks)**

2 Some adults were each asked to write down the number of kilometres they walk each week. Here are the results.

   18   20   13   19   21   10   19   15   19   12   25   16

(a) Write down the mode.

.... **(1 mark)**

(b) Calculate the mean number of kilometres.

....

.... **(2 marks)**

(c) Find the median number of kilometres.

....

.... **(2 marks)**

3 There are 14 children at a party. Here are their weights in kg.

   20.3   16.9   22.4   23.5   18.5   17.2   19.6
   24.6   21.0   15.2   17.9   17.8   16.4   24.1

(a) Find the median weight.

....

.... **(2 marks)**

(b) Work out the mean weight. Give your answer correct to 1 decimal place.

....

.... **(2 marks)**

Averages from frequency tables 1

1 Ella rolls a dice 50 times. She records the information in a frequency table.

Guided

Score	1	2	3	4	5	6
Frequency	7	12	5	11	7	8
Cum freq	7	19				

(a) Write down the mode of the scores.

> Which score occurs most often?

.... **(1 mark)**

(b) Work out the median score.

Median = $\frac{\text{........}}{2}$th number = ...th number

> Use the cumulative frequency to find the median score.

....

.... **(2 marks)**

2 Taran records the ages, in years, of some teenagers at a youth club.
He records the information in a frequency table.

Age	13	14	15	16	17	18	19
Frequency	4	10	9	7	5	4	3

(a) Explain why the mode is 14.

.... **(1 mark)**

(b) Work out the median age.   > Draw an extra row for the cumulative frequencies.

....

.... **(2 marks)**

3 Ben recorded the shoe sizes in his class.
Here is a bar chart to represent the
information.

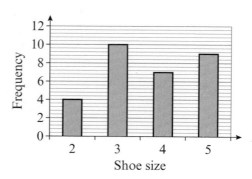

(a) Write down the mode of the shoe sizes.

.... **(1 mark)**

(b) Work out the median shoe size.

....

.... **(2 marks)**

Averages from frequency tables 2

1 Ella rolls a dice 50 times. She records the information in a frequency table.

Guided

Score	1	2	3	4	5	6
Frequency	7	12	4	11	7	9

Work out the mean score. Give your answer correct to 2 decimal places.

$$\text{Mean} = \frac{(1 \times 7) + (2 \times 12) + (3 \times \text{......}) + (4 \times \text{......}) + (\text{......} \times \text{......}) + (\text{......} \times \text{......})}{50}$$

$$= \frac{7 + 24 + \text{.......} + \text{.......} + \text{.......} + \text{.......}}{50}$$

$$= \frac{\text{.......}}{50}$$

$$= \text{.......}$$

(2 marks)

2 Taran records the ages, in years, of some teenagers at a youth club.
He records the information in a frequency table.

Age	13	14	15	16	17	18	19
Frequency	4	10	9	7	5	4	3

Work out the mean age. Give your answer correct to 3 significant figures.

....

....

....

.... **(2 marks)**

3 Ben recorded the shoe sizes in his class.
Here is a bar chart to represent the information.
Work out the mean shoe size. Give your answer correct to 1 decimal place.

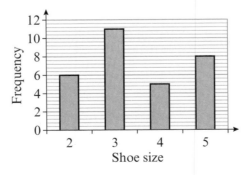

....

....

....

.... **(2 marks)**

Averages from grouped data 1

tier F&H

> **Guided**

1 Jason asked some of his friends the length of time taken, in minutes, to cook lunch on one Sunday afternoon. The table shows some information about his results.

Time taken (in minutes)	Frequency	Cumulative frequency
$10 < t \leq 20$	15	15
$20 < t \leq 30$	12	27
$30 < t \leq 40$	8	35
$40 < t \leq 50$	10	
$50 < t \leq 60$	5	

(a) Write down the modal class.

> The modal class is the interval that occurs the most times.

.... **(1 mark)**

(b) Write down the interval that contains the median.

.... **(1 mark)**

(c) Work out an estimate for the median time taken.
Give your answer correct to 3 significant figures.

Total frequency = 50 so the median is the 25th value.

Estimated median $= 20 + \dfrac{25 - 15}{12} \times 10 = 20 + \dfrac{.......}{12} \times 10 = ...$ minutes   **(2 marks)**

> The 25th value lies in the interval $20 < t \leq 30$.

tier F&H

2 The table shows some information about the prices of 80 second-hand vans that are for sale.

Price (£x)	Frequency
$0 < x \leq 2000$	9
$2000 < x \leq 4000$	12
$4000 < x \leq 6000$	16
$6000 < x \leq 8000$	20
$8000 < x \leq 10\,000$	23

(a) Write down the modal class.

.... **(1 mark)**

(b) Write down the interval that contains the median.

.... **(1 mark)**

(c) Work out an estimate for the median price.

....

....

....

.... **(2 marks)**

Averages from grouped data 2

1 The table shows information about the times, in minutes, taken by some people to get to work.

Guided

Time taken (t minutes)	Frequency	Midpoint	f × midpoint
$10 < t \leq 20$	8	15	8 × 15 = 120
$20 < t \leq 30$	14	25	14 × 25 = 350
$30 < t \leq 40$	17	35	17 × 35 = ...
$40 < t \leq 50$	12	....	.... × .... = ...
$50 < t \leq 60$	9	....	.... × .... = ...

> Extend the table to have two extra columns.

(a) Work out an estimate for the mean time taken. **(3 marks)**

$$\text{Mean} = \frac{120 + 350 + \text{........} + \text{........} + \text{........}}{60} = \frac{\text{........}}{60} = \text{........ minutes}$$

(b) Explain why your answer to part (a) is an estimate.

.... **(1 mark)**

2 The table gives information about the distances, in miles, Ray travelled to deliver 80 parcels.

Distance travelled (m miles)	Frequency		
$0 < m \leq 5$	9		
$5 < m \leq 10$	16		
$10 < m \leq 15$	21		
$15 < m \leq 20$	24		
$20 < m \leq 25$	10		

Work out an estimate for the mean distance.
Give your answer correct to 3 significant figures.

> Extend the table to have two extra columns.

....

....

.... **(3 marks)**

3 Mr Marwaha's class took part in a sponsored swim. The table gives information about the money raised, in £, by each student.

Money raised, x (in £)	Frequency
$0 < x \leq 8$	3
$8 < x \leq 16$	7
$16 < x \leq 24$	9
$24 < x \leq 32$	8
$32 < x \leq 40$	3

Work out an estimate for the mean amount of money raised by the students in Mr Marwaha's class.

....

....

.... **(3 marks)**

Averages from grouped data 3

1 The histogram gives information about the heights, in centimetres, of some plants.

> Guided

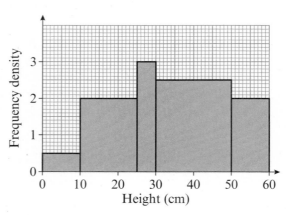

(a) Work out an estimate for the median height.

> Work out the total frequency.

> Find the interval that the median is in.

Total frequency = 0.5 × 10 + 2 × 15 + 3 × .... + ... × .... + ... × ....

= 5 + 30 + ... + ... + ... = ...

Median = $\frac{n}{2}$ = $\frac{.......}{2}$ = ...th value

The median is in the interval 30–50.

Median = 30 + $\frac{....... - 50}{50}$ × 20 = 30 + ... = ...cm **(2 marks)**

(b) Work out an estimate for the mean height.
Give your answer correct to 3 significant figures.

Mean = $\frac{(5 × 5) + (17.5 × 30) + (27.5 × ....) + (40 × ....) + (....... × ....)}{120}$

= $\frac{25 + 525 + ... + ... + ...}{120}$ = $\frac{.......}{120}$ = ...cm **(3 marks)**

2 The histogram gives information about the times taken, in minutes, by a group of students to travel to school in one week.

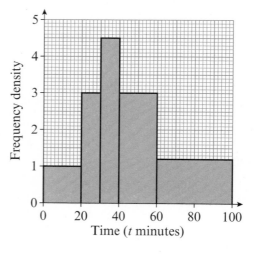

(a) Work out an estimate for the median time. Give your answer correct to 3 significant figures.

....

....

....

....

.... **(2 marks)**

(b) Work out an estimate for the mean time.
Give your answer correct to 3 significant figures.

....

....

.... **(2 marks)**

Transforming data

1 The table shows information about the numbers of visitors to an art gallery during the first week in January.

Day	Mon	Tues	Wed	Thur	Fri	Sat	Sun
Number of visitors	65	10	20	55	60	20	55

Work out:

(a) the mode

.... **(1 mark)**

(b) the median

> Order the frequencies from the lowest to the highest.

....

.... **(2 marks)**

(c) the mean.

....

.... **(2 marks)**

During the second week of January the number of visitors increased by 10% each day compared with the number of visitors in the first week of January.

Write down the new values of:

(d) the mode   (e) the median   (f) the mean

....

.... **(1 mark)**   .... **(1 mark)**   .... **(1 mark)**

> Work out 110% of the mode for the first week of January.

2 Eight friends save money to buy a flat each. The table gives information about the amount of money, to the nearest thousand pounds, saved by each friend in their own deposit account, at the end of 2016.

Friend	A	B	C	D	E	F	G	H
Amount of money (£)	68 000	74 000	42 000	56 000	82 000	48 000	63 000	79 000

(a) Work out the mean.

....

.... **(2 marks)**

At the end of 2017 the amount in each account was 3% more than at the end of 2016.

(b) Work out the mean of the amounts at the end of 2017.

....

.... **(2 marks)**

Geometric mean

1 Find the geometric mean of 25, 32 and 68.

Geometric mean = $\overset{....}{\sqrt{25 \times .... \times ....}}$ = $\overset{....}{\sqrt{............}}$ = ...   **(2 marks)**

Guided

2 Find the geometric mean of 1.65, 1.42, 0.82 and 1.12.

> There are four numbers, so you need to find the 4th root.

....

....

....

....   **(2 marks)**

3 Alan's salary increased from £28 475 to £42 380 over the last 10 years.

(a) Work out the geometric mean of Alan's salaries.

Geometric mean = $\sqrt{28\,475 \times ....}$ = $\sqrt{...........................}$ = ...   **(2 marks)**

Guided

(b) Work out the the average yearly increase in salary.

....

....

....

....   **(2 marks)**

4 Dan buys some shares. The value of the shares increases by 40% in the first year, decreases by 5% in the second year, decreases by 12% in the third year and increases by 18% in the fourth year. Work out the geometric mean and interpret your answer.

> Convert each percentage into a multiplier.

> A 40% increase is a multiplier of 1.40.

....

....

....

....   **(2 marks)**

5 The geometric mean of two numbers is 3.2.
One number is increased by 8% and the other number is decreased by 12%.
Calculate the new geometric mean to 2 decimal places.

....

....

....

....   **(3 marks)**

Weighted mean

1 David sits four tests. Here are his marks and the weighting for each test.

Guided

Test	A	B	C	D
Test mark	65	89	60	62
Weighting	30%	40%	20%	10%

(a) Calculate David's mean test mark.

$$\text{Mean} = \frac{65 + 89 + \text{.......} + \text{.......}}{4} = \frac{\text{.......}}{4} = \text{.......}$$

(1 mark)

(b) Calculate David's weighted mean test mark.

$$\text{Weighted mean} = \frac{(65 \times 30) + (89 \times 40) + (60 \times \text{.......}) + (\text{.......} \times \text{.......})}{30 + 40 + \text{.......} + \text{.......}}$$

$$= \frac{1950 + 3560 + \text{.......} + \text{.......}}{\text{.......}}$$

$$= \frac{\text{..........}}{\text{..........}} = \text{.......}$$

(3 marks)

(c) Explain why there is a difference between the mean test mark and the weighted mean test mark.

.... **(1 mark)**

2 The table gives information about the numbers and values of sales made by two salespeople during the last three weeks.

	Salesperson A			Salesperson B		
	Week 1	Week 2	Week 3	Week 1	Week 2	Week 3
Number of sales	12	18	10	14	16	18
Value of sales (£)	782	459	643	685	421	384

Which salesperson, A or B, had the highest average value per sale overall?

....

....

....

.... **(4 marks)**

3 A painter is making a mixture of different paints.
The table shows the volume, in litres, for each paint.

Paint	A	B	C	D
Weighting	3	4	6	2
Volume (litres)	10	15	x	9

The completed mixture must be 10.4 litres.
Work out the value of x needed for the mixture.

....

....

....

.... **(3 marks)**

Had a go ☐   Nearly there ☐   Nailed it! ☐

Measures of dispersion for discrete data

1 Here are the ages, in years, of 15 children.

12	14	18	15	9	7	12	11
7	11	12	14	15	11	13	

(a) Work out the range.

Range = highest value − lowest value = 18 − .... = ... years   **(2 marks)**

(b) Work out the interquartile range.

> Write out the numbers in numerical order.

Lower quartile = $\frac{1}{4}$(15 + 1)th = 4th value = ...

Upper quartile = $\frac{3}{4}$(15 + 1)th = ...th value = ...

Interquartile range = upper quartile − lower quartile = ... − .... = ... years   **(3 marks)**

2 Tanya recorded the weights, in grams, of 14 wooden blocks.
Here are her results.

22	29	38	16	36	18	30
21	27	25	38	42	79	20

(a) Work out the range.

....

.... **(2 marks)**

(b) Work out the interquartile range.

....

.... **(2 marks)**

(c) Give **one** advantage of using the interquartile range as a measure of spread.

....

.... **(1 mark)**

3 Josh recorded the number of errors on each page of a book.
The table gives information about his results.

Number of errors	0	1	2	3	4	5	6	7
Frequency	6	17	14	9	8	6	4	3

(a) Work out the range.

....

.... **(2 marks)**

(b) Work out the interquartile range.

....

.... **(2 marks)**

Measures of dispersion for grouped data 1

1 The table shows information about the heights, measured to the nearest cm, of 50 plants.

Height (*h* cm)	20 < h ⩽ 30	30 < h ⩽ 40	40 < h ⩽ 50	50 < h ⩽ 60	60 < h ⩽ 70
Frequency	4	7	9	16	14

Calculate an estimate for the range.

> Remember to allow for rounding when finding the minimum and maximum values.

Range = 70.5 − 19.5 = ...cm

(1 mark)

2 The table shows information about the masses, in kilograms, of 60 animals on a farm.

Weight (*w* kilograms)	5 < t ⩽ 15	15 < t ⩽ 25	25 < t ⩽ 35	35 < t ⩽ 45	55 < t ⩽ 65
Frequency	3	13	21	19	4

Use linear interpolation to work out an estimate for

(a) the lower quartile

.... **(1 mark)**

(b) the upper quartile.

.... **(1 mark)**

3 The table shows information about the times, in seconds, of 80 online adverts.

Time (*t* seconds)	0 < t ⩽ 10	10 < t ⩽ 20	20 < t ⩽ 30	30 < t ⩽ 40	40 < t ⩽ 50
Frequency	7	15	26	25	7

(a) On the grid, draw a cumulative frequency graph for this information.

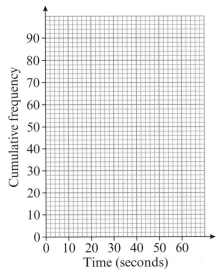

(2 marks)

(b) Use your graph to find an estimate for the lower quartile time of these online adverts.

.... **(1 mark)**

(c) Use your graph to find an estimate for the upper quartile time of these online adverts.

.... **(1 mark)**

Measures of dispersion for grouped data 2

Guided

1   The cumulative frequency graph shows information about the times 80 dogs take to run 200 metres.

Use the cumulative frequency graph to find estimates for

(a) the 30th–70th interpercentile range

70th percentile = 70% × 80th

value = ...th value on the cumulative

　　　　frequency axis

30th percentile = 30% × 80th

value = ...th value on the cumulative

　　　　frequency axis

74 − .... = ... seconds

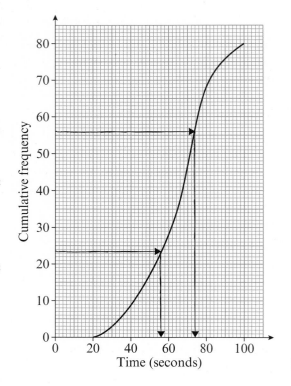

(2 marks)

> Read across from the 70th percentile value to the curve and down to the horizontal axis.

(b) the 2nd–6th interdecile range.

> The 2nd decile is the same as the 20th percentile.

.... **(2 marks)**

(c) (i) Find the 50th percentile.

.... **(1 mark)**

(ii) Interpret your answer to part (c)(i).

.... **(1 mark)**

2   The table shows information about the speeds of some motorbikes.

Speed (s km/h)	$20 < s \leq 40$	$40 < s \leq 60$	$60 < s \leq 80$	$80 < s \leq 100$	$100 < s \leq 120$	$120 < s \leq 140$
Frequency	3	14	34	47	40	12

> Draw a row for the cumulative frequencies.

(a) Estimate the 85th percentile.

.... **(2 marks)**

(b) Estimate the speed exceeded by 85% of the motorbikes.

.... **(2 marks)**

Standard deviation 1

1 Tom recorded the number of points, p, he won on his computer game. He played the game 9 times. Here are his results summarised.

$$\Sigma p = 324 \qquad \Sigma p^2 = 11702$$

Work out

(a) the mean

$$\text{Mean} = \frac{324}{........} = ...\text{ points}$$ **(1 mark)**

(b) the standard deviation. Give your answer correct to 2 decimal places.

$$\text{Standard deviation} = \sqrt{\frac{\Sigma p^2}{n} - \left(\frac{\Sigma p}{n}\right)^2} = \sqrt{\frac{11702}{........} - \left(\frac{324}{........}\right)^2}$$

$$= \sqrt{.................... - (....................)^2}$$

$$= \sqrt{.................... - ....}$$

$$= \sqrt{........} = ...\text{ points}$$ **(2 marks)**

2 Mark was investigating the lengths, in cm, of some bars of metal in his shed. Here are his results.

9.6　10.9　6.2　7.6　10.4　11.1　8.4　8.3　6.9　7.6　6.9　10.1

(a) Show that $\Sigma x^2 = 932.98$

....

.... **(1 mark)**

(b) Find the standard deviation of the lengths of the bars of metal. Give your answer correct to 1 decimal place.

> You are given Σx^2. Work out Σx to use the equation for standard deviation.

....

.... **(2 marks)**

3 Colin measures the heights, in metres, of 12 fully grown apple trees. Here are his results.

1.31　2.7　1.62　1.62　1.46　2.11　1.88　1.10　1.87　1.97　1.66　2.29

(a) Find the mean height.

....

.... **(1 mark)**

(b) Work out the standard deviation. Give your answer correct to 2 significant figures.

....

.... **(1 mark)**

Standard deviation 2

tier H

Guided

1   The distances, m miles, travelled by 140 people to a concert are summarised by the following data.

$\Sigma fx = 4810$ $\Sigma fx^2 = 169\,775$

Calculate estimates of the mean and the standard deviation.

> Standard deviation
> $$= \sqrt{\frac{\Sigma x^2}{n} - \left(\frac{\Sigma x}{n}\right)^2}$$

Mean $= \dfrac{\text{........}}{140} = $ .... miles

$$SD = \sqrt{\frac{\text{................}}{140} - \left(\frac{\text{................}}{140}\right)^2} = \sqrt{\text{................} - (\text{................})^2}$$

$$= \sqrt{\text{................}} = \text{................} \text{ miles}$$

> Don't round until the end.

(3 marks)

tier H

2   David found out the number of rooms in each of 30 houses in a village.
The table shows the information he collected.

Number of rooms (x)	Frequency (f)		
4	3		
5	9		
6	11		
7	5		
8	2		

Work out an estimate of

(a) the mean number of rooms

> Add a third column and label it fx.

....

.... **(1 mark)**

> Add a fourth column and label it fx^2.

(b) the standard deviation of the number of rooms.

....

.... **(2 marks)**

tier H

3   The table gives information about the times spent, in minutes, by 60 adults shopping online last Friday.

Time spent (t minutes)	Frequency		
$0 < t \leqslant 20$	14		
$20 < t \leqslant 50$	30		
$50 < t \leqslant 80$	10		
$80 < t \leqslant 120$	6		

> Add a third and fourth column and label them fx and fx^2 respectively.

> Write down the midpoints in the first column.

Estimate the standard deviation of the times spent shopping online.

....

....

.... **(3 marks)**

Standard deviation 3

1 In an experiment a scientist recorded the lengths, x cm, of 125 worms.
The results are summarised below.

$\Sigma fx = 980$ $\Sigma fx^2 = 10\,126.25$

Find estimates for the mean and the standard deviation.

> Σf means the sum of the frequencies.

$\text{Mean} = \dfrac{\Sigma fx}{\Sigma f} = \dfrac{980}{........} = ... \text{ cm}$

$\text{Standard deviation} = \sqrt{\dfrac{\Sigma fx^2}{\Sigma f} - \left(\dfrac{\Sigma fx}{\Sigma f}\right)^2} = \sqrt{\dfrac{10\,126.25}{........} - \left(\dfrac{980}{........}\right)^2}$

$= \sqrt{.................. - (..................)^2}$

$= \sqrt{..................} = ... \text{ cm}$ **(3 marks)**

2 The table gives information about the times spent, in minutes, by 50 people listening to the radio one Wednesday.

Time spent (in minutes)	Frequency		
$0 < x \leqslant 30$	12		
$30 < x \leqslant 40$	25		
$40 < x \leqslant 60$	8		
$60 < x \leqslant 100$	5		

> Add a third and fourth column and label as fx and fx^2 respectively.

> Write down the midpoints in the first column.

Calculate an estimate for the standard deviation of the distribution.

....

....

....   **(3 marks)**

3 Jeff records the lengths, x cm, of 60 metal poles. The results are summarised in the table.

Length (in cm)	Frequency
$0 < x \leqslant 40$	8
$40 < x \leqslant 60$	15
$60 < x \leqslant 80$	19
$80 < x \leqslant 100$	15
$100 < x \leqslant 180$	3

(a) Work out an estimate of the mean length.

....

....   **(2 marks)**

(b) Work out an estimate of the standard deviation.

....

....   **(2 marks)**

(c) Explain why your values for the mean and standard deviation are estimates.

....   **(1 mark)**

53

Had a go ☐ Nearly there ☐ Nailed it! ☐

Box plots

1 A group of students took a general knowledge test with 20 questions.
The table shows information about the times, in minutes, they took to complete the test.

Guided

	Least	LQ	Median	UQ	Greatest
Time in minutes	13	19	23	29	33

On the grid, draw a box plot to show the information in the table.

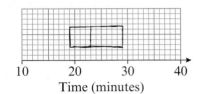

Time (minutes)

(3 marks)

2 Here are the lengths, in centimetres, of 15 pieces of rope.

21	25	31	38	39	41	42	46
47	50	53	54	55	56	61	

Guided

On the grid, draw a box plot to show this information.

(3 marks)

> Make sure a suitable scale is used on the horizontal axis.

Lower quartile = $\frac{1}{4}$(15 + 1)th = 4th value = ...

Median = $\frac{1}{2}$(15 + 1)th = 8th value = ...

Upper quartile = $\frac{3}{4}$(15 + 1)th = ...th value = ...

Highest value = ...cm

Lowest value = ...cm

3 Cody measured the lengths of some nails, in cm, to 1 decimal place.
Here are her results.

11.3	15.8	12.4	13.5	11.6	15.8	12.7	13.6	14.8	11.4
12.9	13.4	15.7	11.5	15.1	14.9	15.2	12.7	13.4	

On the grid, draw a box plot to show the information.

....

....

(3 marks)

Outliers

1 A scientist records the amount of rainfall, in mm, over a period of 15 days. Here are her results.

39	27	42	38	42	23	43	25
43	32	32	30	31	41	102	

She works out that the summary statistics are $\Sigma x = 590$ and $\Sigma x^2 = 28\,068$
Use this information to identify any outliers.

$$\text{Mean} = \frac{\Sigma x}{n} = \frac{\dots\dots}{\dots\dots} = \dots\dots \text{ mm}$$

$$\text{Standard deviation} = \sqrt{\frac{\Sigma x^2}{n} - \left(\frac{\Sigma x}{n}\right)^2} = \sqrt{\frac{\dots\dots\dots\dots}{\dots\dots\dots\dots} - (39.33\dots)^2} = \sqrt{\dots\dots\dots\dots} = \dots\dots \text{ mm}$$

Outliers are outside the range: mean $\pm$ (3 × SD)

= .... − (3 × ....) to .... + (3 × ....)

= .... to ....

> The outliers are the numbers that are outside this range.

.... **(3 marks)**

2 Tom recorded the weights, to the nearest kilogram, of some children. Here are his results.

23	35	41	47	49	50	50	53
54	57	59	60	62	63	65	

> Use the IQR definition to find the outliers. An outlier is less than $Q_1 − 1.5 \times$ IQR or greater than $Q_3 − 1.5 \times$ IQR.

(a) Show that 23 is an outlier.

....

.... **(3 marks)**

(b) On the grid, draw a box plot to show the information.

(3 marks)

3 Joseph played 19 games on his phone. He recorded the points he scored. Here are his results.

17	29	33	36	36	34	38	39	40	41
43	43	46	48	48	52	55	58	69	

> Use the IQR definition to find the outliers.

(a) Identify any outliers.

....

.... **(3 marks)**

(b) On the grid, draw a box plot to show the information.

(3 marks)

Skewness

1 The box plot below shows information about the times, in minutes, some people took to complete a puzzle.

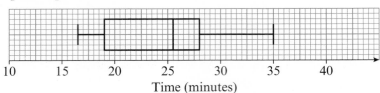

Time (minutes)

Describe the skew. Give a reason.

> Compare the value of the median – LQ with the value of the UQ – median.

....

.... **(1 mark)**

2 Tom goes to work. The number of minutes he is early to work over a 15-day working period is shown below.

| 2 | 2 | 2 | 2 | 5 | 8 | 9 | 10 |

| 12 | 16 | 19 | 24 | 29 | 30 | 31 |

(a) Find the mean, mode and median of this set of data.

....

....

....

.... **(3 marks)**

(b) Using the mean, mode and median, describe the skew.

....

.... **(2 marks)**

(c) Interpret your answer to part (b).

....

.... **(1 mark)**

3 A box contains six counters numbered 1, 2, 3, 4, 5 and 6. A counter is drawn from the box and the number recorded. The counter is returned to the box each time, and this is repeated 100 times.

Here are the results: Mean = 3.81, mode = 5, median = 4

(a) Using the mean, mode and median, describe the skew.

....

.... **(2 marks)**

(b) Interpret your answer to part (a).

....

.... **(1 mark)**

Deciding which average to use

1 Alex asked 9 friends how many text messages they each sent last week. Here are his results.

22   11   9   10   14   8   19   5   62

(a) Find

(i) the median

> Rewrite the results in ascending order.

5 8 9 10 11 14 19 22 62

12.05

(ii) the mean.

17.78

(2 marks)

(b) Which average is the most appropriate to use for this information? You must give a reason.

The mean is the most appropriate it provide more accurate representation. The median is effected out liers   **(1 mark)**

(c) Explain why the mode cannot be found.

no number repeat   **(1 mark)**

2 In a survey of pay at a large manufacturing company, it is found that the average pay of a manager is £38 452. Another survey at the same company finds that the average pay of a shopfloor worker is £23 568.
The managing director of the company says that both figures are correct.
Explain why they might both be correct.

Both the median and the mean could have been calculated

(2 marks)

3 Mr Wenger told each student their individual exam mark and then gave the exam statistics to the whole class. He told the class the modal mark, the median mark and the mean mark.

(a) Which average would tell a student whether they were in the top half or the bottom half of the class?

median   **(1 mark)**

(b) Which average allows a student to work out how well they have done compared with other students in the class?

mean   **(1 mark)**

4 Mike counts the number of nails in each of 11 boxes. Here are his results:

37   38   40   40   40   ⟨41⟩   42   43   43   44   44

On the box it says that the average content is 42 nails.
Is this correct? Explain your answer.

> Work out the mean, median and mode.

Mode: 40   median 41   37.45

(3 marks)

Comparing data sets

1 The box plots show the ages of some people waiting to see a doctor at Penn Surgery and at Himley Surgery.

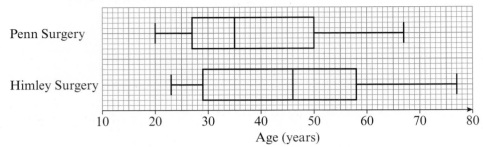

Penn Surgery

Himley Surgery

Age (years)

Compare the distribution of the ages of people at Penn Surgery with the distribution of the ages of people at Himley Surgery.
Write down **three** comparisons.

1 The median age is lower at Penn Surgery.

> Make a comparison about
> the range or the IQR.

> Give a contextualised comparison
> between the two surgeries.

2 ....

3 .... **(3 marks)**

2 The back-to-back stem and leaf diagram shows the speeds, in miles per hour (mph), of cars on road X and on road Y.

Road X		Road Y
	2	7 7 9
6 5 2	**3**	0 2 3 5 6 9
7 7 6 4	**4**	2 4 6 7
9 7 6 3 0	**5**	0 2
6 3 2	**6**	

Key: 2|3 represents 32 mph   2|7 represents 27 mph

Compare the two distributions. Write down **three** comparisons.

1 ....

2 ....

3 .... **(3 marks)**

3 The table gives the mean and the standard deviation of the marks in two examinations.

	Mean	Standard deviation
Music	65.7	3.5
Drama	58.3	5.2

Compare the distribution of the marks for music with the distribution of the marks for drama and interpret in context.

....

.... **(2 marks)**

Making estimates

1 The box plot shows information about the amounts of money, in £, spent by some adults in one evening.

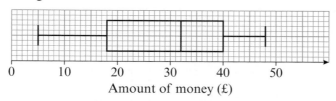

Amount of money (£)

(a) What proportion of the adults spent more than £40?

> Each quartile is 25%.

.... **(1 mark)**

The total number of adults is 260.

(b) Estimate the number of adults who spent

   (i) more than £32

....

....

   (ii) less than £18.

....

.... **(2 marks)**

2 Andy records the marks (m) that some children obtain in a test.
The maximum mark is 80.

Percentile	10	20	30	40	50	60	70	80	90	100
Marks (m)	9	15	24	32	39	48	56	61	72	80

(a) What percentage of these children scored 48 marks or more?

.... **(1 mark)**

The same test is given to another 2000 children.

(b) Work out the number of children who are expected to score 24 marks or fewer.

....

....

....

.... **(2 marks)**

3 Boris pays his gas bill in 12 monthly payments. The interquartile range of the monthly payments is £34.
The 75th percentile of the monthly payments is £142.
Work out the 25th percentile of the monthly payments.

....

....

....

.... **(2 marks)**

Scatter diagrams

1 The table below shows the amount of petrol used by a car and the distance driven on 8 different journeys.

Distance (km)	75	140	197	180	20	92	105	43
Petrol (litres)	8	12.5	23.5	17	3	8.5	10	4

(a) Explain why a scatter diagram is suitable for this data.

A scatter diagram is suitable because this is .... data.   **(1 mark)**

(b) Plot this data on a scatter diagram.

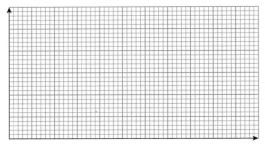

(3 marks)

(c) Is there an association between the distance travelled and the amount of petrol used?

....

....   **(1 mark)**

2 The table below shows the resting heart rate (beats per minute) and the number of hours of exercise per week, for 8 adults.

Resting heart rate (bpm)	72	90	80	65	60	55	87	75
Hours of exercise per week	8	4	6	12	10	11	3	7

(a) Which variable should be plotted on the horizontal axis?
Give a reason for your answer.

....

....   **(2 marks)**

(b) Plot this data on a scatter diagram.

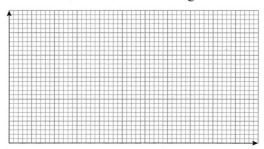

(3 marks)

(c) Is there an association between resting heart rate and the number of hours of exercise?

....

....   **(1 mark)**

Correlation

1 A car rental company has cars with different engine sizes, measured in litres.
The company records the number of miles travelled by cars of different engine sizes, using one gallon of petrol.
The scatter diagram shows this information.

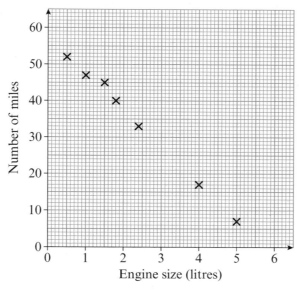

The company buys two new cars with different engine sizes.
The table shows the miles travelled using one gallon of petrol for these cars.

Engine size (litres)	3.2	4.7
Number of miles	25	15

(a) Use the information in the table to complete the scatter diagram. **(1 mark)**

(b) Describe the correlation between the engine size and the number of miles.

.... **(1 mark)**

(c) Describe the relationship between the engine size and the number of miles.

.... **(1 mark)**

2 Mr Smith's students did a maths test and a science test. The scatter diagram shows the marks of 12 of these students.

Describe the relationship between the maths mark and the science mark.

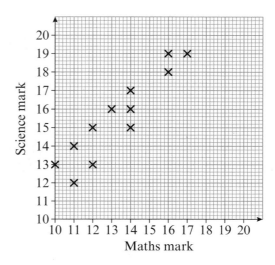

.... **(1 mark)**

Causal relationships

Guided

1 Sandeep owns a coffee shop in Wolverhampton. The scatter diagram shows the maximum temperature in degrees Celsius (°C) in Wolverhampton and the number of hot chocolate drinks sold on each of 8 days.

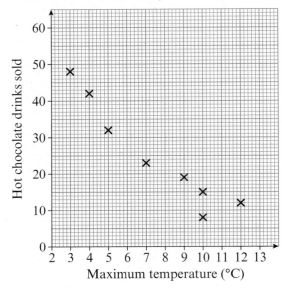

(a) Do you think there is a causal relationship between the maximum temperature and the number of hot chocolate drinks sold? Give a reason for your answer.

There is probably a causal relationship between the maximum temperature and

the number of hot chocolates sold because ....

.... **(2 marks)**

(b) How strong is the correlation? Give a possible reason for this.

.... **(2 marks)**

2 The scatter diagram shows some information about the length of some twigs, in cm, and the length of hand spans of some toddlers, in cm.

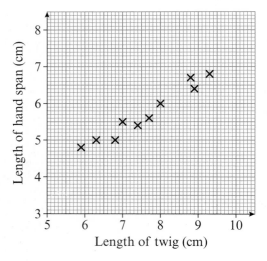

(a) Describe the correlation.

.... **(1 mark)**

(b) Do you think there is a causal relationship between the length of twigs and the length of hand spans of toddlers? Give a reason for your answer.

....

.... **(2 marks)**

Line of best fit

> **Guided**

1 The table shows the time taken and the distance travelled by a taxi driver for 10 journeys.

Distance (km)	1.7	8.4	5.3	6.6	4.8	7.1	3.8	2.8	8.7	5.5
Time (minutes)	4	18	12	14	10	16	9	6	17	11

(a) Complete the scatter diagram to show this information.

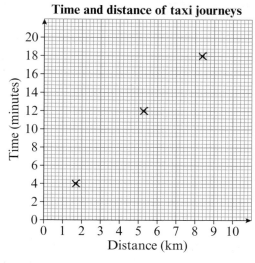

Time and distance of taxi journeys

(3 marks)

(b) Draw a line of best fit on the scatter diagram.　(1 mark)

On another occasion the taxi driver takes 13 minutes for a journey.

(c) Use your line of best fit to estimate the distance travelled by the taxi driver.

(1 mark)

2 The table shows the marks for 8 students in mathematics and in physics.

Mathematics	11	21	29	41	51	55	63	75
Physics	22	26	37	42	50	61	73	82

(a) Plot a scatter diagram to show this information.

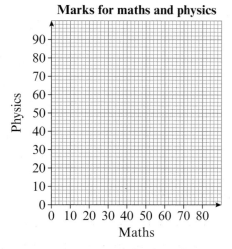

Marks for maths and physics

(3 marks)

(b) Find the mean point and plot it on the scatter diagram.　(2 marks)

> For the mean point, find the mean of the x-values and the mean of the y-values.

(c) Draw a line of best fit using the mean point.　(1 mark)

Had a go ☐ **Nearly there** ☐ **Nailed it!** ☐

Interpolation and extrapolation

1 A garage sells motorbikes.
The scatter diagram shows information about the price and age of 8 motorbikes.

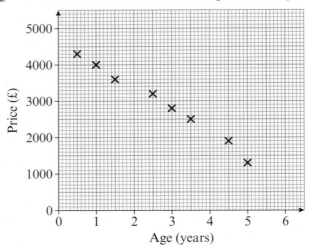

A motorbike is 4 years old and has a price of £2200.

(a) Use the information to complete the scatter diagram. **(1 mark)**

(b) Describe and interpret the correlation.

....

.... **(2 marks)**

The mean point of the data is (2.8, 2900).

(c) (i) Plot the mean point on the scatter diagram.

(ii) Draw a line of best fit through the mean point. **(2 marks)**

A motorbike is 2 years old.

(d) (i) Estimate the price of this motorbike.

....

(ii) Is this estimate likely to be reliable? Give a reason for your answer.

....

.... **(3 marks)**

Another motorbike is 6 years old.

(e) (i) Estimate the price of this motorbike.

....

(ii) Is this estimate likely to be reliable? Give a reason for your answer.

....

.... **(3 marks)**

The equation of a line of best fit 1

1 Lucas tested his comprehension skills over a nine-week period.
The scatter diagram shows the number of errors he made and the number of minutes he practised each week.

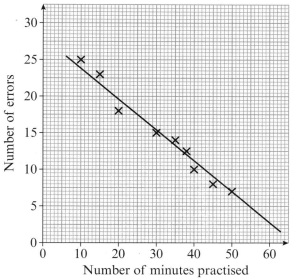

A line of best fit is drawn on the scatter diagram.

(a) Describe the relationship shown by the scatter diagram.

.... **(1 mark)**

(b) Calculate the gradient of the line of best fit.

> Choose two points on the line of best fit and draw a right-angled triangle. The gradient $= \dfrac{\text{height}}{\text{base}}$

....

....

.... **(2 marks)**

The equation of the line of best fit has the form $y = ax + b$ where x is the number of minutes practised and y is the number of errors.

(c) (i) Write down the equation of the line of best fit in the form $y = ax + b$

....

(ii) Interpret the value of a and the value of b.

....

....

.... **(4 marks)**

The next week, Lucas practices for 63 minutes.
Making a prediction to find the number of errors Lucas makes in his next test by using the line of best fit may not be reliable.

(d) Explain why.

.... **(1 mark)**

The equation of a line of best fit 2

1 The scatter diagram shows information about the height and the arm length of each of 8 children.
The equation of the regression line is $y = 0.652x - 13.6$.

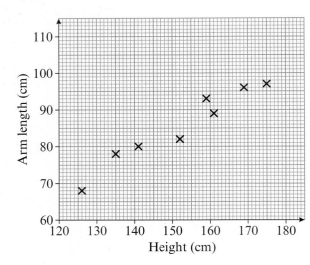

(a) Draw this line on the scatter diagram. **(2 marks)**

> Calculate the coordinates of two points on the regression line. Choose values of x within the range of data given.

When $x = 130$, $y = 0.652 \times 130 - 13.6 = 71.16 \approx 71$

When $x = 170$, $y = 0.652 \times 170 - 13.6 = ... \approx ....$

(b) Interpret the value of the gradient of the regression line.

.... **(1 mark)**

2 The scatter diagram shows information about 10 flats in a city. The diagram shows the distance from the city centre and the monthly rent of each flat. The equation of the regression line is $y = 550 - 117x$.

(a) Draw the regression line on the scatter diagram.

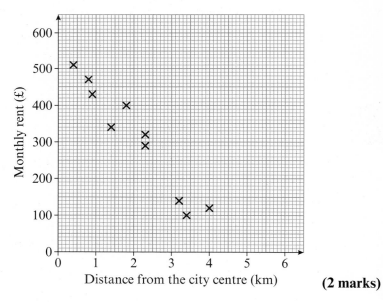

(2 marks)

(b) Interpret the value of the gradient of the line.

.... **(1 mark)**

(c) Use the equation of the regression line to predict the monthly rent of a flat which is 10 km from the city centre. Comment on the reliability of your answer.

....

.... **(2 marks)**

Spearman's rank correlation coefficient

1   A coach recorded the results of the athletes at a club. She ranked the results and then calculated the Spearman's rank correlation coefficient (SRCC) between each pair of events.
Here are the results.

Events	Long jump / High jump	Shot put / Pole vault	Shot put / 100 m sprint
SRCC	0.85	−0.45	0

Comment on the value of the Spearman's rank correlation coefficient between

(a) long jump and high jump

Strong .... correlation   **(1 mark)**

(b) shot put and pole vault

.... **(1 mark)**

(c) shot put and 100 m sprint.

.... **(1 mark)**

2   John is training for a swimming gala. He trains over a 10-week period and records his best time for 100 m each week. His training and 100 m times were ranked, and the Spearman's rank correlation coefficient was calculated.
The Spearman's rank correlation coefficient was −0.72.
Describe and interpret the value of the Spearman's rank correlation coefficient.

....

....

.... **(2 marks)**

3   Tom and Jerry were judges on a dancing competition. They scored the dancers on Rumba dancing and Salsa dancing. The scores were ranked and the Spearman's rank correlation coefficient was calculated between their scores. Here are the results.

Dance	Rumba	Salsa
SRCC	0.92	0.68

Comment on the agreement between Tom's and Jerry's scores.

....

....

.... **(2 marks)**

Calculating Spearman's rank correlation coefficient

1 Ravina and Anjali each ranked 10 cakes at a village fete. Here are their ranks.

> **Guided**

Cake	A	B	C	D	E	F	G	H	I	J
Ravina	1	9	3	6	8	2	7	4	10	5
Anjali	8	4	7	1	3	5	10	9	6	2
d	7	5	4	5	5					
d^2	49	25	16	25	25					

Determine how much agreement there is between Ravina and Anjali.
Show your calculations.

$$r_s = 1 - \frac{6\Sigma d^2}{n(n^2 - 1)}$$

$$= 1 - \frac{6 \times (49 + 25 + 16 + 25 + 25 + \text{.......} + \text{.......} + \text{.......} + \text{.......} + \text{.......})}{10(10^2 - 1)}$$

$$= 1 - \frac{6 \times (\text{.............})}{\text{.............}} = 1 - \frac{\text{.............}}{\text{.............}}$$

$$= 1 - \text{.............} = \text{.............}$$

(5 marks)

2 Two critics watched the same 8 theatre shows. They were then asked to rank the shows in order of preference. The table gives information about their ranks.

Show	A	B	C	D	E	F	G	H
Critic 1	3	8	7	4	5	1	2	6
Critic 2	1	6	7	5	4	3	2	8

Determine how much agreement there is between the critics.
Show your calculations.

....

....

....

....

....

.... **(5 marks)**

Pearson's product moment correlation coefficient

1 Jason is investigating the relationship between the amount of fertiliser used, x, and the weight of his tomatoes, y. The scatter diagram shows this information.

Jason calculated two correlation coefficients. Here are some possible results.

Spearman's rank correlation coefficient	−0.85	−0.65	0	0.65	(0.85)
Pearson's product moment correlation coefficient	−0.85	−0.65	0	0.65	0.85

(a) Circle one value from each row to show the most likely pair of correlation coefficients for this data. **(2 marks)**

(b) Explain your answers in part (a).

....

....

.... **(1 mark)**

2 A clothes shop manager records the weekly sales figures and the average weekly temperature, $t\,°C$, for 6 weeks during the summer.

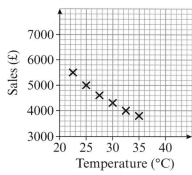

The manager works out two correlation coefficients: −0.87   −0.90

(a) Complete the table.

Spearman's rank correlation coefficient	
Pearson's product moment correlation coefficient	

(2 marks)

(b) Give a reason for your answers in part (a).

....

.... **(2 marks)**

Line graphs and time series

1 The table shows information about the population of a village (in thousands).

Year	1985	1990	1995	2000	2005	2010
Population (1000s)	6	8	9	13	10	11

Guided

(a) Draw a time series graph for this information.

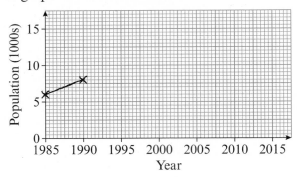

(2 marks)

(b) (i) Write down the year with the highest population.

....

(ii) Work out the population increase from 1985 to 2000.

....

.... **(2 marks)**

2 The time series graph gives information about the number of vehicles rented from a garage each quarter for 2015 and 2016.

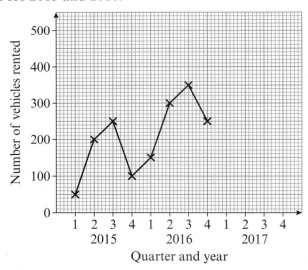

Here are the results for 2017.

Quarter	1	2	3	4
Number of vehicles rented	320	360	470	140

(a) Plot this information on the time series graph. **(2 marks)**

(b) Compare and interpret the variation in the number of vehicles rented for each quarter in the years 2015, 2016 and 2017.

....

.... **(2 marks)**

Trend lines

1 The incomplete time series graph shows quarterly electricity bills paid by a householder over 2015 and 2016.

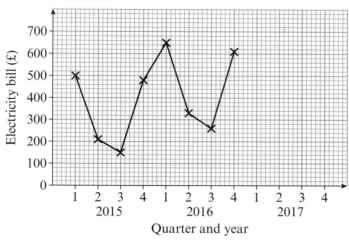

Here is some information for the year 2017.

Quarter	1	2	3	4
Electricity bill, £	690	402	332	640

(a) Use the table to complete the time series graph.   **(2 marks)**

(b) Draw a trend line for the data on the time series graph.   **(1 mark)**

> The trend line should be drawn roughly half way between the highest and lowest points for each year.

(c) Describe and interpret the trend in the electricity bills paid from 2015 to 2017.

....

.... **(2 marks)**

2 The time series graph shows the number of steel girders sold at a builders' merchants in 2015 and 2016.

Here is some information for the year 2017.

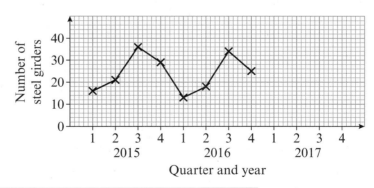

Quarter	1	2	3	4
Number of steel girders sold	9	14	29	21

(a) Use the table to complete the time series graph.   **(2 marks)**

(b) Draw a trend line on the graph.   **(1 mark)**

(c) Describe and interpret the trend in the number of steel girders sold from 2015 to 2017.

....

.... **(2 marks)**

Variations in a time series

1 The incomplete time series graph gives information about the total amount of money spent by customers on cold drinks in a newsagent's each quarter for the years 2015 and 2016.

Guided

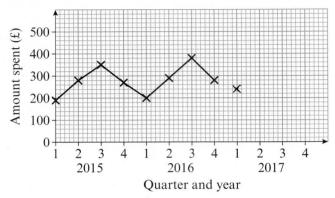

The table shows the equivalent information for 2017.

Quarter	1	2	3	4
Amount spent (£)	240	350	420	320

(a) Use the information in the table to complete the time series graph. **(2 marks)**

(b) Draw a trend line on the graph. **(1 mark)**

(c) Describe the variations shown in the graph.
Suggest a reason why these seasonal variations take place.

....

.... **(2 marks)**

2 The time series graph gives information about the sales of hot chocolate drinks at a market stall over three years.

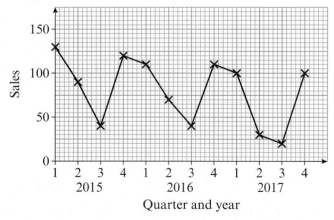

(a) Draw a trend line on the graph. **(1 mark)**

(b) Describe the variations shown in the graph.
Suggest a reason why these seasonal variations take place.

....

.... **(2 marks)**

Moving averages 1

1 The table shows the numbers of bolts, to the nearest hundred, made in a small factory over a two-year period.

	2016				2017			
Quarter	1	2	3	4	1	2	3	4
Number of bolts	2700	6000	2800	1600	2500	5400	2600	1500

(a) Work out the 4-point moving averages for this information.

First moving average $= \dfrac{2700 + 6000 + 2800 + 1600}{4} = \dfrac{\dots}{4} = \dots$

....

....

....

....

....

.... **(2 marks)**

(b) Describe the trend in the number of bolts made in the factory.

.... **(1 mark)**

2 The table shows information about the number of new cars sold each month by a garage.

Month	Jan	Feb	Mar	Apr	May	Jun	Jul	Aug
Number of new cars	10	7	22	25	22	24	29	28

(a) Work out the 3-point moving averages for this information.

First moving average $= \dfrac{10 + 7 + 22}{3} = \dfrac{\dots}{3} = \dots$

....

....

....

....

....

.... **(2 marks)**

(b) Describe the trend in the number of new cars sold by the garage from January to August.

.... **(1 mark)**

Moving averages 2

Guided

1 The table gives information about the number of motorbikes sold by JR Autos each quarter over three years.

	2016				2017				2018			
Quarter	1	2	3	4	1	2	3	4	1	2	3	4
Number of sales	31	51	46	36	34	54	47	38	36	55	49	41

(a) Use the information in the table to draw a time series graph. **(3 marks)**

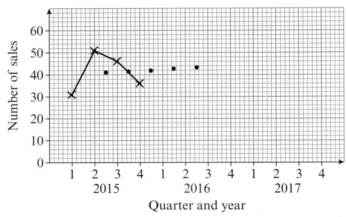

The first five 4-point moving averages are

     41, 41.75, 42.5, 42.75, 43.25

(b) (i) Work out the last four 4-point moving averages.

....

....

....

....

....

....

....

....

     (ii) Plot these moving averages on the time series graph. **(4 marks)**

(c) Draw a trend line for the moving averages. **(1 mark)**

(d) Describe and interpret the trend.

....

.... **(2 marks)**

Seasonal variations

1 The table graph gives some information about the numbers of customers visiting a garden centre for the years 2015 to 2017.

	2015				2016				2017			
Quarter	1	2	3	4	1	2	3	4	1	2	3	4
Number of customers (thousands)	10	16	20	14	12	17	21	15	19	21	24	22
4-point moving average		15	15.5	15.75	16	16.25	18	19				

(a) Use the information in the table to draw a time series graph.

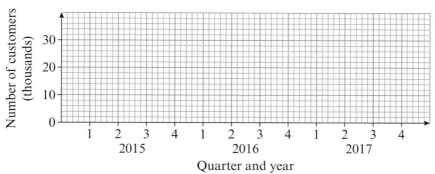

(3 marks)

The last two 4-point moving averages are missing from the table.

(b) (i) Calculate the last two 4-point moving averages.
     Write your answers in the table.

....

....

....

    (ii) Plot all the 4-point moving averages on the time series graph. **(4 marks)**

(c) Draw a trend line for the moving averages. **(1 mark)**

(d) In which quarter was the number of customers visiting the garden centre the least?

.... **(1 mark)**

(e) Use the trend line and the mean seasonal variation to predict the number of customers visiting the garden centre in the first quarter of 2018.

....

....

.... **(4 marks)**

The manager wants to use the information to predict the number of customers who will visit the garden centre in 2019.

(f) Discuss whether or not it would be appropriate to do this.

....

.... **(2 marks)**

The meaning of probability 1

1 (a) Write down a word from the box that best describes the likelihood of each outcome below.

impossible	unlikely	evens	likely	certain

(i) In a week chosen at random, Friday will be after Thursday.

....

(ii) A fair coin will show tails when flipped once.

.... **(2 marks)**

(b) James rolls an ordinary fair dice.

(i) On the probability scale, mark with a cross (×) the probability that the dice will land on a number greater than 6.

```
0          0.5          1
```

> Remember that 0 is impossible and 1 is certain.

(ii) On the probability scale, mark with a cross (×) the probability that the dice will land on an even number.

```
0          0.5          1
```
(2 marks)

2 A box contains only 5 black counters and 1 white counter. One counter is to be taken at random from the box. Here is a list of words:

impossible   unlikely   evens   likely   certain

Use one word from the list to complete each sentence below.

(a) The outcome 'the counter is black' is .... **(1 mark)**

(b) The outcome 'the counter is yellow' is .... **(1 mark)**

3 Here is a list of probabilities:

0   0.2   0.5   0.8   1

Complete the table by matching each probability to its probability word.

Probability word	likely	evens	certain	unlikely	impossible
Probability					

(2 marks)

4 There are 4 beads in a bag. 2 beads are black, 1 bead is red and 1 bead is green. Isla takes a bead at random from the bag.

(a) On the probability scale, mark with a cross (×) the probability that Isla will take a black bead.

```
0          0.5          1
```
(1 mark)

(b) On the probability scale, mark with a cross (×) the probability that Isla will take a green bead.

```
0          0.5          1
```
(1 mark)

The meaning of probability 2

1 Here are 9 cards. Each card has a letter on it.

| A | A | A | A | B | B | B | C | C |

Carl takes a card at random. Find the probability that Carl takes a card with the letter

(a) A

$$P(A) = \frac{\text{number of successful outcomes}}{\text{total number of possible outcomes}} = \frac{\text{.......}}{9}$$

(2 marks)

(b) C.

....

.... **(2 marks)**

2 A box contains some coloured cards.
In the box there 2 red cards, 3 blue cards and 5 yellow cards.
Taran takes a card at random from the box.

(a) Work out the probability that Taran takes a blue card.

> Work out the total number of outcomes by adding up all the cards.

....

.... **(2 marks)**

Taran replaces his card in the box.
Ella takes a card from the box and then replaces the card. Ella does this 80 times.

(b) Work out an estimate for the number of times Ella takes a red card.

....

.... **(2 marks)**

3 Here is a fair 5-sided spinner.
Kate spins the spinner 50 times.
Work out an estimate for the number of times the spinner lands on red.

....

....

.... **(2 marks)**

Spinner sections: Red, Orange, Blue, Yellow, Red

4 There are 60 beads in a bag. 25 of the beads are red, 20 of the beads are blue and 5 of the beads are green. The rest of the beads are yellow.
Jessica takes a bead at random from the bag. What is the probability that the bead is

(a) blue?

.... **(2 marks)**

(b) white?

.... **(1 mark)**

(c) yellow?

.... **(2 marks)**

77

The meaning of probability 3

Guided

1 The two-way table shows the distribution of members of the audience at the theatre.

	Type of seating			
	Stalls	**Circle**	**Balcony**	**Total**
Adults	36	39		112
Children	41	21	31	
Total	77	60		

(a) Complete the two-way table. **(2 marks)**

(b) Write down the total number of members of the audience.

.... **(1 mark)**

One of the members of the audience is picked at random.

(c) Write down the probability that the person picked is

(i) a child

$$P(\text{Child}) = \frac{\text{number of children}}{\text{total number of members}} = \frac{........}{........}$$

(ii) an adult sitting in the balcony.

....

.... **(4 marks)**

2 Some students visited a museum over three days. The two-way table shows some information about these students.

	Monday	**Wednesday**	**Friday**	**Total**
Boys			16	43
Girls	21			
Total		34	30	100

(a) Complete the two-way table. **(2 marks)**

One of the students is picked at random.

(b) Write down the probability that this student

(i) visited the museum on Monday

....

(ii) is a girl who visited the museum on Friday

....

....

(iii) is a girl or a boy who visited the museum on Wednesday.

....

.... **(4 marks)**

Experimental probability

1 Nicola has a biased coin. She flips the coin 45 times and records the numbers of heads and tails. Her results are:

Heads	28
Tails	17

Guided

(a) Estimate the probability that Nicola will get a head when she flips the coin again.

$$P(H) = \frac{\text{number of heads}}{\text{total number of flips}} = \frac{........}{45}$$

(1 mark)

(b) How can Nicola improve her estimate?

....   **(1 mark)**

2 Alex and Rebecca want to estimate the probability that a student in their school picked at random has blue eyes. Alex takes a random sample of 30 students in the school. He finds that 6 of the students have blue eyes.
A student is picked at random.

(a) Using Alex's results, write down an estimate for the probability that the student has blue eyes.

....

....   **(1 mark)**

Rebecca takes a random sample of 120 students in the school. Using her results, her estimate of the probability that a student in the school has blue eyes is 0.15.

(b) Discuss which of Alex or Rebecca is likely to have a better estimate for the probability that a student in their school has blue eyes. Give a reason for your answer.

....

....

....   **(2 marks)**

3 Hannah rolls a 4-sided dice 50 times. On each roll, the dice can land on 1, 2, 3 or 4. Here are her results.

Score	1	2	3	4
Frequency	4	32	5	9

Hannah is going to roll the 4-sided dice again.

(a) Use the results in the table to find an estimate of the probability that the dice will land on 2.

....

....   **(1 mark)**

Hannah concludes that the 4-sided dice is most likely to land on a score of 2 the next time it is rolled.

(b) Comment on the reliability of Hannah's conclusion.

....

....   **(2 marks)**

Using probability to assess risk

Guided

1   The two-way table shows some information about some chemists in a laboratory.

	Attended a Health and Safety course	Did not attend a Health and Safety course	Total
Accident	4	34	
No accident	36	56	
Total	40	90	

Use the information in the table to work out

(a) the relative risk of a chemist who has not attended the Health and Safety course having an accident compared with a chemist who has attended the Health and Safety course.
Give your answer correct to 3 significant figures.

$$\text{Relative risk} = \frac{\text{risk for those in the group}}{\text{risk for those not in the group}} = \frac{\frac{34}{90}}{\frac{......}{......}} = ... \div .... = ...$$ **(3 marks)**

(b) the absolute risk of a chemist having an accident in the laboratory.
Give your answer correct to 3 significant figures.

....

....   **(1 mark)**

2   In a canteen, two vending machines, A and B, dispense drinks. The table shows the number of times each vending machine did not dispense a drink one afternoon owing to an error in the machine.

Machine	Did not dispense	Did dispense	Total
A	3	27	30
B	6	84	90

(a) Work out the relative risk of A not dispensing a drink compared with B not dispensing a drink.

....

....

....

....

....   **(3 marks)**

Jenna states that the risk of A not dispensing a drink is greater than the risk of B not dispensing a drink.

(b) Is Jenna correct? You must give a reason.

....

....

....

....   **(2 marks)**

Sample space diagrams

1 Carol has two fair 6-sided dice, A and B. She is going to roll both dice once.

(a) Complete the sample space diagram to show all the possible outcomes.

		Dice B					
		1	**2**	**3**	**4**	**5**	**6**
	1	(1,1)	(1,2)	(1,3)	(1,4)	(1,5)	(1,6)
	2	(2,1)	(2,2)	(2,3)	(2,4)	(2,5)	(2,6)
Dice A	**3**	(3,1)	(3,2)	(3,3)	(3,4)	(3,5)	(3,6)
	4	(4,1)	(4,2)	(4,3)	(4,4)		
	5	(5,1)	(5,2)	(5,3)			
	6	(6,1)	(6,2)	(6,3)			

(b) Write down the probability that Carol will get a 2 on one dice and a 3 on the other dice.

$$P(2,3) = \frac{\text{number of ways of getting 2 on one dice and 3 on the other dice}}{\text{total number of outcomes}}$$

$$= \frac{\text{.......} + \text{.......}}{6 \times \text{.......}} = \frac{\text{.......}}{\text{.......}} = \frac{\text{.......}}{\text{.......}}$$

(1 mark)

(c) Work out the probability of getting a total of 8.

....

.... **(2 marks)**

Carol rolls dice A once and dice B once.

(d) Compare the probability that Carol will get a total of 4 with the probability that she will get a total of 9.

....

.... **(2 marks)**

2 Rosie has two fair spinners.
One is a 5-sided spinner, which can land on 2 or on 4 or on 6 or on 8 or on 10.
The other is a 4-sided spinner, which can land on 1 or on 2 or on 3 or on 4.
Rosie is going to spin each spinner once. Her score is the sum of the two numbers she gets. The sample space diagram shows some of the possible scores.

		5-sided spinner				
		2	**4**	**6**	**8**	**10**
	1	3	5	7	9	11
4-sided	**2**	4	6	8	10	12
spinner	**3**	5	7			
	4	6	8			

(a) Complete the sample space diagram to show all the possible scores. **(1 mark)**

(b) (i) Find the probability that the score will be 7.

....

    (ii) Find the probability that the score will be less than 8.

.... **(2 marks)**

Venn diagrams

tier F&H

⟩ Guided ⟩

1 In a group of 40 friends, 18 play football, 21 play cricket, 11 play football and cricket.

(a) Complete the Venn diagram.

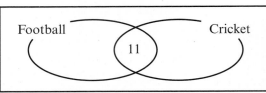

> Always start from the overlap and then work your way outwards to complete the Venn diagram.

(2 marks)

(b) Work out the probability that a friend selected at random:

(i) plays only football

$$P(\text{Plays only football}) = \frac{\text{number of friends who play only football}}{\text{total number of friends}} = \frac{\text{........}}{40}$$

(ii) plays only cricket

....

....

(iii) plays football or cricket but not both

....

....

(iv) does not play football or cricket.

....

.... **(6 marks)**

tier F&H

2 Here are the results of a survey on the types of exercise taken by a group of 100 people.

66 run, 47 swim, 60 cycle, 34 run and swim, 31 swim and cycle, 36 run and cycle, 24 do all three

(a) Complete the Venn diagram to represent this information.

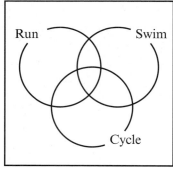

(2 marks)

(b) Work out the probability that a randomly selected person from the survey

(i) does none of these types of exercise

....

....

(ii) swims but does not run.

....

.... **(4 marks)**

Mutually exclusive and exhaustive events

1 Here are 10 cards.

| 10 | | 10 | | 15 | | 15 | | 15 | | 30 | | 30 | | 30 | | 30 | | 40 |

Picking an even number and picking an odd number are mutually exclusive events.

(a) Explain what is meant by the term 'mutually exclusive'.

> Can mutually exclusive events happen at the same time or not?

.... **(1 mark)**

Anjali picks one of these cards at random.

(b) (i) Find the probability that this card has a 10 or a 30 on it.

$$P(10 \text{ or } 30) = \frac{\text{number of cards with } 10 + \text{number of cards with } 30}{\text{total number of cards}}$$

$$= \frac{\text{........} + \text{........}}{10} = \frac{\text{........}}{10} = \frac{\text{........}}{\text{........}}$$ **(1 mark)**

(ii) Find the probability that this card does **not** have a 15 on it.

.... **(1 mark)**

2 The Venn diagram shows probabilities relating to two events, X and Y. Explain whether or not X and Y are exhaustive events.

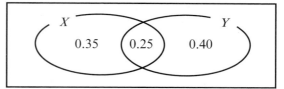

.... **(1 mark)**

3 Chris has a box containing red, blue, green and yellow counters. The table shows the probabilities that the colour shown will be red or will be blue or will be yellow.

Colour	Red	Blue	Green	Yellow
Probability	0.20	0.14		0.30

Chris takes a counter at random from the box.

(a) Find the probability that he will pick a green counter.

> The sum of all the probabilities is 1.

.... **(2 marks)**

(b) Find the probability that he will pick a red counter or a blue counter.

.... **(2 marks)**

(c) Find the probability that he will pick a counter that is **not** yellow.

.... **(2 marks)**

The general addition law

1 Given that P(*A*) = 0.35, P(*B*) = 0.45 and P(*A* and *B*) = 0.12, find P(*A* or *B*).

> **Guided**

P(A or B) = P(A) + P(B) − P(A and B) = 0.35 + 0.45 − 0.12 = ...   **(2 marks)**

2 *A* and *B* are two events and P(*A*) = 0.5, P(*B*) = 0.6 and P(*A* or *B*) = 0.9.
Work out:

(a) P(*A'*)

> *A'* means *A* does not happen.

....
....   **(2 marks)**

(b) P(*A* and *B*).

....
....   **(2 marks)**

3 *A* and *B* are two events and P(*A*) = 0.6, P(*B*) = 0.2 and P(*A* and *B*) = 0.1.
Work out:

(a) P(*B'*)

....
....   **(2 marks)**

(b) P(*A* or *B*).

....
....   **(2 marks)**

4 The probability that a child has green eyes is 0.64.
The probability that a child has brown hair is 0.57.
The probability that a child has green eyes or brown hair or both is 0.79.
A child is picked at random. Work out the probability that the child has:

(a) green eyes and brown hair

....
....   **(2 marks)**

(b) neither green eyes nor brown hair.

....
....   **(2 marks)**

5 A survey shows that 80% of the households in Penn own a lawnmower, 55% own a strimmer and 40% of the households own both. A household is selected at random.
Work out the probability the household has neither a lawnmower nor a strimmer.

....
....   **(3 marks)**

Independent events

1 Events A and B are independent. $P(A) = 0.2$ and $P(B) = 0.65$.
Work out

Guided

(a) $P(A \text{ and } B)$

$P(A \text{ and } B) = P(A) \times P(B) = \dots\dots \times \dots\dots = \dots\dots$ **(2 marks)**

(b) $P(A \text{ or } B)$.

....

....

....   **(3 marks)**

2 A bag contains 12 beads. 7 are black and 5 are white. A bead is taken from the bag at random, the colour is recorded and the bead is replaced. A second bead is then taken from the bag at random and its colour is recorded.

(a) Work out the probability that both beads are black.

....

....   **(2 marks)**

(b) Work out the probability that one bead is black and the other bead is white.

....

....   **(2 marks)**

3 Two events A and B are such that $P(A) = 0.3$, $P(B) = 0.4$ and $P(A \text{ or } B) = 0.58$.

(a) Work out $P(A \text{ and } B)$.

....

....   **(2 marks)**

(b) Show that A and B are independent events.

....

....   **(2 marks)**

4 The Venn diagram shows probabilities relating to two events, X and Y.

(a) Work out $P(X) \times P(Y)$.

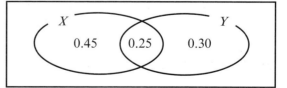

....

....

....   **(2 marks)**

(b) Are the events X and Y independent?

....

....

....   **(2 marks)**

Had a go ☐ Nearly there ☐ Nailed it! ☐

Tree diagrams

1 Tom and Anil each take a driving test. The probability that Tom will pass his driving test is 0.6. The probability that Anil will pass his driving test is 0.7.

> **Guided**

    (a) Draw a tree diagram to represent this information.

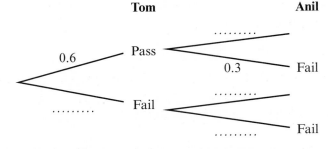

Write the outcomes and the probability of each outcome on the branches of the tree diagram.

Tom   **Anil**

             0.6 Pass   ....

                   0.3   Fail

           .... Fail   ....

                   .... Fail

                                  (3 marks)

    (b) Work out the probability that both Tom and Anil will not pass.

    P(Tom fails) = 1 − .... = ...

    P(Anil fails) = 0.3

    P(Tom fails and Anil fails) = ... × .... = ...   **(2 marks)**

    (c) Work out the probability that Tom or Anil, but not both of them, will pass.

Use the tree branches with 1 pass and 1 fail in any order.

    ....

    .... **(2 marks)**

2 A farmer supplies organic chickens and standard chickens. 35% of the chickens are organic. The rest are standard chickens. If a chicken does not meet a particular weight, it cannot be sold.
10% of the organic chickens cannot be sold.
15% of the standard chickens cannot be sold.

    (a) Draw a tree diagram to represent this information.   **(3 marks)**

    A chicken is picked at random.

    (b) Find the probability that it cannot be sold.

    ....

    .... **(3 marks)**

    One of the chickens that cannot be sold is picked at random.

    (c) Find the probability that it is an organic chicken.

    ....

    .... **(2 marks)**

Conditional probability

Guided

1 The table shows information about some children in a school.

Gender		Right handed	Left handed	Ambidextrous	Total
	Boys	30		16	84
	Girls	8		30	86
	Total	38			170

(a) Complete the two-way table. **(2 marks)**

A child is picked at random.

(b) Write down the probability that the child is a girl who is left handed.

$$P(\text{Girl and left handed}) = \frac{\text{number of girls who are left handed}}{\text{total number of children}} = \frac{\text{..........}}{170}$$ **(1 mark)**

(c) Given that the child is right handed, work out the probability that this child is a boy.

....

.... **(2 marks)**

Another child is picked at random.

(d) Given that the child is a girl, work out the probability that this child is ambidextrous.

....

.... **(2 marks)**

2 In a block of flats, 70% of people own smartphones. 40% of these smartphone owners also own tablets. 80% of those who are not smartphone owners are tablet owners.

(a) Draw a tree diagram for this information. **(3 marks)**

A person is selected at random.

(b) Find the probability that the person does not own a tablet, given that this person is a smartphone owner.

....

.... **(2 marks)**

(c) Find the probability that the person owns a smartphone and a tablet.

....

.... **(2 marks)**

The formula for conditional probability

1 The Venn diagram shows the number of students in a class who got 75% or more on two mathematics tests.

> **Guided**

Let A represent the event 'a student gets 75% or more on test 1'.

Let B represent the event 'a student gets 75% or more on test 2'.

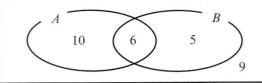

(a) Work out P(A).

$$P(A) = \frac{10 + ...}{........ + ... + ... + ...} = \frac{.........}{.........} = \frac{.........}{.........}$$ **(1 mark)**

(b) Work out P($A \mid B$).

$$P(A \mid B) = \frac{P(A \text{ and } B)}{P(B)} = \frac{\frac{.........}{.........}}{\frac{.........}{.........}} = \frac{.........}{.........}$$ **(2 marks)**

(c) Using your answers to parts (a) and (b), explain whether or not A and B are independent events.

....

....   **(2 marks)**

2 Two events are such that P(A) = 0.3, P(B) = 0.4 and P(A or B) = 0.55. Work out:

(a) P(A and B)

....

....   **(2 marks)**

(b) P($A \mid B$)

....

....   **(2 marks)**

3 Two boxes, A and B, contain some red and green beads. Box A contains 20 red beads and 5 green beads. Box B contains 18 red beads and 12 green beads. There are no other beads in the boxes. Tony selects one of the boxes at random then picks a bead from the box at random.

(a) Draw a probability tree diagram for this information.

(3 marks)

(b) Find the probability of

(i) a red bead being picked

....

(ii) a red bead being picked, given that box A is selected.

....   **(2 marks)**

Index numbers

1 In 2014 a laptop cost £600. Using 2014 as the base year, the index number for the cost of a laptop in 2016 was 108.
How much did the laptop cost in 2016?

> The index number for a year is that year's price as a percentage of the base year price.

$600 \times \dfrac{108}{100} = 600 \times \dots\dots\dots = \dots\dots\dots$

(2 marks)

2 Jim was working out the price index of a bag of coal at his local hardware shop. With 2016 as the base year, the price index for a bag of coal in 2018 was 109.

(a) Describe the change in the price of a bag of coal between 2016 and 2018.

> An index number greater than 100 indicates an increase.

....

.... **(2 marks)**

The price of a bag of wooden logs at the hardware shop decreased by 1.5% from its 2016 price.

(b) With 2016 as the base year, write down the price index for a bag of wooden logs in 2018. Give your answer correct to 1 decimal place.

.... **(1 mark)**

3 The table shows the average monthly rental price for a property in Northern Ireland.

Year	2017	2018
Average monthly rental price (£)	614	629

Source: homelet.co.uk/homelet-rental-index

(a) Using 2017 as the base year, calculate the index number for the average monthly rental price in 2018. Give your answer correct to 1 decimal place.

....

.... **(2 marks)**

The index number for the average monthly rental price for a property in Scotland for the same period was 105.6.

(b) Compare how the monthly rental prices changed from 2017 to 2018 for properties in Northern Ireland and in Scotland.

....

.... **(2 marks)**

RPI and CPI

1 The table shows information about the retail price index (RPI) and the price, in £, of a seven-day travel card for the London Underground for 2005, 2010 and 2015.

> Guided

	2005	2010	2015
RPI	100	116	135
Travel card price (£)	30.40	36.80	46.10

Sources: Office for National Statistics and londonist.com

Compare the increase in the price of a travel card with the increase in the RPI over the five years from 2005 to 2010, and over the ten years from 2005 to 2015.

2005 to 2010: Percentage increase in RPI = 116% − 100% = ...

Percentage increase in travel card price = $\dfrac{36.80 - 30.40}{30.40} \times 100$ = ...

2005 to 2015: Percentage increase in RPI = ...% − ....% = ...

Percentage increase in travel card price = $\dfrac{.......... - ....}{..........} \times 100$ = ...

....

....　**(5 marks)**

2 The table shows information about the consumer price index (CPI) and the price, in £, of a calculator for 2005, 2010 and 2015.

	2005	2010	2015
CPI	100	114	128
Calculator price (£)	5.20	6.10	6.50

Source: Office for National Statistics

Compare the increase in the price of a calculator with the increase in the CPI over the five years from 2005 to 2010, and over the ten years from 2005 to 2015.

....

....

....　**(5 marks)**

3 The table shows information about the retail price index (RPI), consumer price index (CPI) and the price, in pence, of first class stamps for 1990, 2000 and 2010.

	1990	2000	2010
RPI	100	135	177
CPI	100	130	160
Price of stamp (pence)	22	27	39

Which price index, CPI or RPI, does the price of a stamp follow over the 20 years from 1990 to 2010? You must justify your answer.

....

....

....　**(4 marks)**

GDP

> **Guided**

1 The table shows the quarterly growth in GDP for the UK as a percentage.

	2014				**2015**				**2016**			
Quarter	1	2	3	4	1	2	3	4	1	2	3	4
Percentage	0.8	0.9	0.7	0.7	0.4	0.6	0.4	0.7	0.3	0.2	0.5	0.7

Source: Office for National Statistics

(a) Which quarter and year had

   (i) the greatest quarterly growth

Quarter: 2   Year: ....

   (ii) the least quarterly growth?

.... **(2 marks)**

(b) Which year had the greatest average growth? You must show your working.

....

.... **(2 marks)**

2 The bar chart shows the growth in GDP (%) per year for Ecuador, Japan and Tunisia from 2007 to 2010.

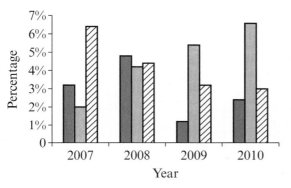

Sources:
Cabinet Office, Japan;
Banco Central del Ecuador;
National Institute of Statistics, Tunisia

(a) Describe the trend for Japan.

.... **(1 mark)**

(b) Which country has seen its GDP decrease every year?

.... **(1 mark)**

(c) Write down the year in which Ecuador, Japan and Tunisia had a similar growth in GDP.

.... **(1 mark)**

3 The table shows the changes in UK GDP for the last quarter in 2017.

Sector of economy	Agriculture	Manufacturing	Services
% change from previous quarter	0.4	0.3	0.6

Manufacturing generates 10% of UK GDP and agriculture generates 1% of UK GDP. Meghan says, 'The percentage increases in manufacturing and agriculture were very similar, so manufacturing and agriculture increased GDP by the same amount'. Is Meghan correct? You must give a reason.

....

....

....

.... **(4 marks)**

Weighted index numbers

1 A company produces nails and bolts.
The table gives information about the nails and bolts it makes.

Product	Weighting	Index in 2013	Index in 2018
Nails	65%	100	92
Bolts	35%	100	87

(a) Using 2013 as the base year, work out the weighted index number for the products for 2018.

Weighted Index number $= \dfrac{\Sigma wx}{\Sigma w} = \dfrac{(65 \times 92) + (\ldots\ldots \times \ldots\ldots)}{65 + \ldots\ldots}$

$= \dfrac{\ldots\ldots + \ldots\ldots}{\ldots\ldots} = \dfrac{\ldots\ldots}{\ldots\ldots} = \ldots\ldots$ **(3 marks)**

(b) Interpret your answer to part (a).

> An index number less than 100 indicates a decrease.

.... **(1 mark)**

2 A company makes Babbitt metal, which is an alloy. Babbitt metal is made by combining three metals, tin, antimony and copper, in the ratio $16:3:1$. The table shows the index number for the cost of each metal in 2018, using 2015 as the base year.

Metal	Tin	Antimony	Copper
Weighting	16	3	1
Index number	104.6	107.4	112.3

The company claims that the combined cost of the metals in the alloy has increased by over 5% between 2015 and 2018. Is the company right? You must give reasons.

....

....

.... **(4 marks)**

3 A company owns two shops. The table gives information about the cost per item from the two shops in 2017 and 2018.

Year	2017	2018
Shop A	£50	£58
Shop B	£65	£72

The ratio of the number of items from shop A to the number of items from shop B is $4:1$.

(a) Using 2017 as the base year, work out the weighted index number for the costs for 2018. Give your answer correct to 1 decimal place.

....

....

.... **(4 marks)**

(b) Interpret your answer to part (a).

.... **(1 mark)**

Chain base index numbers

1 The table shows the value, in pounds, of a necklace for the years 2015 to 2018. The table also gives the chain base index number for 2016, correct to 1 decimal place, for this value.

> **Guided**

Year	2015	2016	2017	2018
Value (£)	2100	2400	2600	2900
Chain base index number		114.3		

(a) Interpret the value 114.3 in the table.

Percentage increase = 114.3 − 100 = ... **(1 mark)**

(b) Calculate, correct to 1 decimal place, the chain base index numbers for 2017 and 2018.

Chain base index number for 2017 = $\dfrac{2600}{2400}$ × 100 = ... × 100

= ....

Chain base index number for 2018 = $\dfrac{..........}{..........}$ × 100 = ... × 100

= .... **(2 marks)**

(c) Using your answers to part (b), calculate the geometric mean of the three chain base index numbers. Give your answer correct to 1 decimal place.

Geometric mean = $\sqrt[3]{114.3 \times .... \times ....}$ = ... **(2 marks)**

(d) Give an interpretation of your answer to part (c).

.... **(1 mark)**

2 Brett bought a motorbike in January. The table shows the value of Brett's motorbike for the months January to May. The table also gives the chain base index numbers, correct to 1 decimal place, for February and for March.

Month	Jan	Feb	Mar	Apr	May
Value (£)	21 000	20 000	18 400	18 000	17 800
Chain base index number		95.2	92.0		

(a) Calculate the chain base index numbers for April and for May, and write them in the table. Give your answers correct to 1 decimal place.

....

.... **(2 marks)**

(b) Calculate the geometric mean of the chain base index numbers for February, March, April and May. Give your answer correct to 1 decimal place.

....

.... **(2 marks)**

(c) Describe what the geometric mean shows about the value of the motorbike during this period.

.... **(1 mark)**

Had a go ☐   Nearly there ☐   Nailed it! ☐

Crude rates

1 The population of Smallville was 25 000 at the start of 2017.
During this year there were 260 deaths and 215 births in the town.

Guided

(a) Find:

(i) the crude death rate per thousand

> The formula is given on the examination papers.

Crude death rate = $\dfrac{260}{25\,000}$ × .... = ...

(ii) the crude birth rate per thousand.

....

.... **(3 marks)**

(b) Work out the population of Smallville at the end of 2017.

.... **(1 mark)**

(c) In 2018 the crude birth rate per thousand was 7.2.
How many births were there in 2018?

....

.... **(2 marks)**

2 The following table shows the number of deaths in one year in each of two towns, Pennhouse and Wells.

Guided

Age group	Pennhouse			Wells		
	Population	Deaths	Death rate	Population	Deaths	Death rate
Under 16	2250	12	5.3	1125	4	
16–40	6000	44	7.3	3000	20	
41–70	3750	56	14.9	7500	120	
Over 70	750	80	106.7	2250	170	

(a) Work out the death rate for each age group in Wells.
Give your answers correct to 1 decimal place. Write your answers in the table.

.... **(3 marks)**

(b) Work out the crude death rate for Wells.
Give your answer correct to 1 decimal place.

> Use your answers to part (a).

Total population = 1125 + 3000 + ... + ... = ...

Crude death rate = $\left(3.6 \times \dfrac{1125}{13\,875}\right) + \left(6.7 \times \dfrac{\text{..........}}{13\,875}\right) + \left(16 \times \dfrac{\text{..........}}{\text{..........}}\right)$

$+ \left(\text{..........} \times \dfrac{\text{..........}}{\text{..........}}\right)$

$= (3.6 \times 0.0811) + (6.7 \times \text{..........}) + (16 \times \text{..........}) + (\text{..........} \times \text{..........})$

$= \text{..........} + \text{..........} + \text{..........} + \text{..........} = \text{..........}$ **(2 marks)**

The crude death rate for Pennhouse is 15.1.

(c) Compare and contrast the crude death rates for Pennhouse and Wells.

....

.... **(2 marks)**

Standardised rates

1 Janice is investigating the number of deaths in different age groups.
The table shows information about the number of deaths in Eastside village.

Age group	Eastside		Standard population
	Population	**Deaths**	
Under 16	3000	6	25%
16–35	12 000	18	35%
36–65	10 000	8	30%
Over 65	4000	60	10%

(a) Work out the standardised death rate for Eastside.
Give your answer correct to 1 decimal place.

> Work out the death rate for each age group.

Under 16 age group: $\dfrac{6}{3000}$ × 1000 = 2

16–35 age group: $\dfrac{18}{\text{..........}}$ × 1000 = ...

36–65 age group: $\dfrac{\text{..........}}{\text{..............}}$ × .... = ...

Over 65 age group: $\dfrac{\text{..........}}{\text{..............}}$ × .... = ...

Standardised death rate = death rate × standard population

Standardised death rate = (2 × 0.25) + (1.5 × ....) + (.......... × ....)

+ (.......... × ....)

= .... + ... + ... + ... = ...   **(3 marks)**

(b) What is the advantage of Janice quoting the standardised death rate for Eastside rather than the crude death rate?

....

....   **(1 mark)**

(c) Westside village has a standardised death rate of 8.9 per 1000 people. In which of these villages would you prefer to live? Give a reason for your answer.

....

....   **(1 mark)**

Binomial distributions 1

1 There are 14 marbles in a bag. 9 of the marbles are white. 5 of the marbles are black. Nav takes a marble at random from the bag. He records the colour of the marble and puts it back in the bag. Elaine takes a marble at random from the bag.

Guided

(a) Work out the probability that two white marbles are taken.

> Work out the probability of taking a white marble from the bag.

$$\frac{9}{14} \times \frac{\dotsb}{\dotsb} = \frac{\dotsb}{\dotsb}$$

(2 marks)

(b) Write down the probability that marbles of different colours are taken.

> Write down all the ways of getting different coloured marbles.

P(Different colours) = P(White and black) + P(Black and white)

$$= \left(\frac{9}{14} \times \frac{\dotsb}{\dotsb}\right) + \left(\frac{\dotsb}{\dotsb} \times \frac{\dotsb}{\dotsb}\right)$$

$$= \frac{\dotsb}{\dotsb} + \frac{\dotsb}{\dotsb} = \frac{\dotsb}{\dotsb} = \frac{\dotsb}{\dotsb}$$

(3 marks)

2 Rohan has a biased 6-sided dice. When the dice is rolled once, the probability that it will land on 6 is 0.3. Rohan is going to roll the dice twice.
Work out the probability that the dice will land on 6 exactly once.

....

....

.... **(3 marks)**

3 Chloe has a spinner. The spinner can land on yellow or on blue. The probability that the spinner will land on yellow is 0.65. Chloe spins the spinner twice.
Work out the probability that the spinner lands on two different colours.

....

....

.... **(3 marks)**

4 There are 7 mint flavoured sweets and 3 chocolate flavoured sweets in a box.
Amelia takes 1 sweet at random from the box. She writes down its flavour, and puts it back in the box.
Amelia then takes a second sweet at random from the box.
Let X = number of mint flavoured sweets taken from the box.
Complete the probability distribution of X.

X	0	1	2
P(X)			

....

....

.... **(4 marks)**

Binomial distributions 2

1 Priya is a telesales agent.
The probability that Priya makes a sale on a customer call is 0.2.
Priya makes 5 customer calls.

Guided

(a) State **two** assumptions that are required to model the number of sales on a customer call in a random sample of size 5 as a binomial distribution.

> Always answer in the context of the question.

1 Fixed number of customer calls

2 .... **(2 marks)**

(b) Work out the probability that Priya makes no sales from the 5 customer calls.

....
.... **(2 marks)**

(c) Work out the probability that Priya makes sales from more than half of the 5 customer calls.

....
....
.... **(3 marks)**

2 In a cafe an average of 1 out of every 5 customers ask for sparkling water with their lunch. A random sample of 10 customers is selected.

(a) Estimate the mean number of customers who ask for sparkling water with their lunch.

.... **(1 mark)**

(b) Find the probability that exactly 1 asks for sparkling water with their lunch.

....
.... **(2 marks)**

(c) Find the probability that fewer than 3 ask for sparkling water with their lunch.

....
....
.... **(3 marks)**

A second random sample of n customers is selected. The probability that at least one of these n customers will have sparkling water with their lunch is greater than 0.95.

(d) What can you conclude, if anything, about the value of n?
You must show your working.

....
....
.... **(3 marks)**

Normal distributions

1 Tom sells two types of statues. The mean height of the wooden statues is 72 cm and the standard deviation is 3 cm. The mean height of the metal statues is 60 cm and the standard deviation is 5 cm. The heights of each type of statue are normally distributed. On the grid, sketch the two normal distributions.

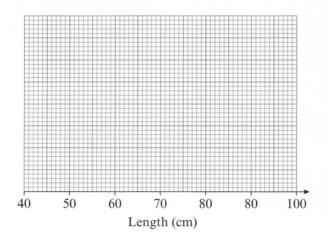

Length (cm)

> Sketch a bell-shaped curve centred on the mean and ending at 3 standard deviations from the mean.

> Sketch 3 standard deviations either side of the mean.

> The curve with the larger range has the smaller maximum height.

(4 marks)

2 A batch of batteries has a mean life of 1500 minutes and a standard deviation of 25 minutes.

> Guided

(a) Write down the probability distribution that can be used to model the lifetime of a battery. Give a reason why this model is suitable.

.... distribution because the data is .... **(2 marks)**

(b) Work out the probability that a battery selected at random will

   (i) last between 1475 minutes and 1525 minutes

> Work out the number of standard deviations from the mean.

> Recall the percentage of the population for 1, 2 and 3 standard deviations from the mean.

....

....

   (ii) last more than 1550 minutes.

....

.... **(4 marks)**

200 batteries are tested.

(c) Estimate the number of batteries that last less than 1450 minutes.

....

....

.... **(3 marks)**

Standardised scores

1 A total of 60 adults took a test. The mark, x, for each adult was recorded. Here is a summary of the results.

$$\Sigma x = 5400 \qquad \Sigma x^2 = 489\,840$$

Jordan got a mark of 78.
Work out the standardised score of Jordan's mark.

> Work out the mean and the standard deviation.

Mean $= \dfrac{\Sigma x}{n} = \dfrac{\text{..........}}{\text{..........}} = \text{..........}$

Standard deviation $= \sqrt{\dfrac{\Sigma x^2}{n} - \left(\dfrac{\Sigma x}{n}\right)^2} = \sqrt{\dfrac{\text{..........}}{\text{..........}} - \left(\dfrac{\text{..........}}{\text{..........}}\right)^2}$

$\qquad\qquad = \sqrt{\text{..........} - (\text{..........})^2} = \sqrt{\text{..........} - \text{..........}} = \sqrt{\text{..........}} = \text{..........}$

Standardised score $= \dfrac{\text{mark} - \text{mean}}{\text{standard deviation}} = \dfrac{\text{........} - \text{........}}{\text{........}} = \dfrac{\text{........}}{\text{........}} = \text{........}$ **(4 marks)**

2 The distances jumped in a ski jumping competition are normally distributed with a mean of 120 m and a standard deviation of 5 m. Faisal jumped a distance of 124 m in this competition.

(a) Calculate the standardised score for Faisal's jump.

....

.... **(2 marks)**

Roxy and Asha each jumped in this competition. The standardised score for Roxy's jump is −1.20 and the standardised score for Asha's jump is −1.15.

(b) Who jumped further in the competition, Roxy or Asha? Give a reason for your answer.

.... **(1 mark)**

(c) Work out the distance jumped by Roxy.

....

.... **(2 marks)**

3 Jess competed in the javelin and the long jump at a school athletics competition. Jess thinks the scores may be modelled by normal distributions. The distances thrown in the javelin competition have a mean of 54 m and a standard deviation of 4 m. Jess threw a distance of 61 m in the competition.

(a) Calculate the standardised score of Jess's throw.

....

.... **(2 marks)**

Jess had a standardised score of −1.2 for the long jump.

(b) Compare the performance of Jess in the javelin with her performance in the long jump.

....

.... **(2 marks)**

Quality assurance and control charts 1

1 A company produces chocolate bars with a target weight of 84 g. For quality control, random samples are taken to check that the production line is working correctly. The mean weights for the samples are normally distributed with a mean of 84 g and a standard deviation of 2 g. A quality control chart is used to plot the sample mean weights.

The lower warning limit and the lower action limit have been drawn on the chart.

(a) Complete the control chart by adding the upper warning limit and the upper action limit. Label your lines.

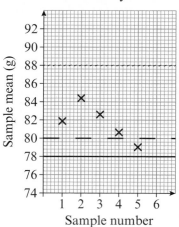

> To draw **warning** limits use:
> mean ± 2 standard deviations
> To draw **action** limits use:
> mean ± 3 standard deviations

(2 marks)

Five sample means have been plotted on the control chart.
Sample 6 has a mean weight of 76.8 g.

(b) (i) Plot this sample mean on the control chart.

> Plot the point at (6, 76.8).

(ii) Describe the action that now needs to be taken.

....

.... **(2 marks)**

2 A company makes nails on a production line in a factory. The production line is set so that the sample means should be normally distributed with a mean of 52 mm and a standard deviation of 0.5 mm. Anna takes the samples in order to monitor the sample means of the weights.
Here is her incomplete control chart showing 6 sample means.
By completing the control chart, determine what actions, if any, Anna should have taken based on the information given.
You must justify your answer.

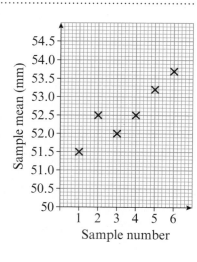

....

....

....

.... **(6 marks)**

Quality assurance and control charts 2

1 A hot chocolate machine is designed to produce 120 millilitres of hot chocolate per serving. For quality control, random samples of three servings are taken and the range of each sample is found. A quality control chart is used to plot the sample ranges. The first five sample ranges have been plotted.

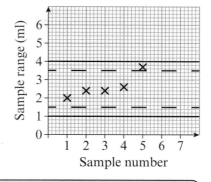

(a) Describe what action should be taken after the fifth sample.

> Look to see if the 5th point falls between the warning and action limits or outside the action limits.

.... **(1 mark)**

The amounts of hot chocolate, in millilitres, in the sixth sample are:

118.5   122.7   121.8

(b) (i) Work out the value of the sample range for this sample.

    ....

    (ii) Plot this sample range on the quality control chart.

    (iii) Describe what action should be taken after the sixth sample.

    ....

.... **(3 marks)**

2 A machine is used to fill packets with rice. The sample medians are normally distributed with a median of 160 g and a standard deviation of 4 g. The manager takes the samples in order to monitor the sample medians of the weights.

(a) Write down the limits when the sample medians lie in the following percentages.

    (i) 95%

.... **(1 mark)**

    (ii) 99.8%

.... **(1 mark)**

The manager finds the sample median of the weights. Each sample median is then plotted on the control chart.

(b) By drawing the warning and action lines, comment what action should be taken by the manager.

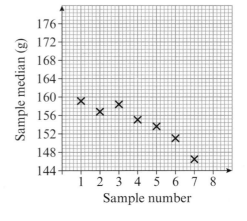

....

....

....

.... **(4 marks)**

Answers

COLLECTING DATA

1. Describing data

 1 Continuous, discrete, categorical

2 Any one from: continuous data because it can take any value in a given interval or range; continuous data because it is a measurement of a physical quantity.

3 Quantitative, continuous

4 (a) discrete
(b) continuous
(c) bivariate
(d) ordinal

5 Any suitable related data: price of car, type of fuel, make of car, model of car, insurance group, road tax, carbon emissions, etc.

2. Primary and secondary data

1 Secondary data because it has been collected by someone else.

2 Primary data is data that you collect.
Secondary data is data that you use but that has been collected by someone else.

3 (a) Any two from: data may not be up to date, data may not be in the required format, some data may be missing, reliability of the website is not known.
(b) May not have access to European or African men.

4 Reliability is known and secondary data is not relevant.

5 Adults from 100 years ago are not alive so their heights cannot be measured, so secondary data must be used. Adults now can be measured so primary data could be used for these.

3. Collecting data 1

1

Colour	Tally	Frequency
Red		
Black		
White		
Blue		
Yellow		

2

Type of vegetable	Tally	Frequency

3

Number of goals	Tally	Frequency
1	||||	4
2	ⅢⅡ	5
3	ⅢⅡ|	6
4	ⅢⅡ	5

4

Age of car (in years)	Tally	Frequency
0 to less than 2		
2 to less than 4		
4 to less than 6		
6 or more		

4. Collecting data 2

 1 (a) Explanatory: fertiliser. Response: size of tomatoes
(b) Advantage: the amount of fertiliser can be controlled and the size of the tomato measured.
Disadvantage: tomato plants may grow differently in a controlled environment compared with real-life growing conditions.

2 (a) Explanatory: new drug. Response: severity of acne
(b) Laboratory
(c) Cannot control people's reaction to the new drug.

3 Controlling extraneous variables as all dogs are in the same conditions, all the data is recorded by the same person so less likelihood of recording errors, the experiment is easily replicated.

5. Collecting data 3

 1 (a) Explanatory: weedkiller. Response: number of weeds in the lawn
(b) Field
(c) Advantage: more likely to reflect real-life behaviour.
Disadvantage: cannot control extraneous variables.
(d) Any two from: the results may be affected by different types of weeds, new weeds growing, varying weather conditions.

2 (a) (i) Altitude of the city
(ii) Average winter temperature
(b) Extreme weather

6. Problems with collected data

1 (a) Any two from: data given in different formats; remove extraneous symbols; remove anomalies/outliers; data given in wrong order.
(b) Rewrite the Gender as M and F; rewrite the times as digits only (e.g. rewrite Ninety-one as 91).
(c) Student could have left out the value or this could mean that they have not done any reading during the week.
(d) Any two from: large sample size increases reliability; issues due to the way the data collection is carried out may decrease reliability (e.g. recorded by students and not by Pierre); students may make mistakes in typing information; the week of the study may be not a typical week for reading for some students (e.g. some students may be reading more than average for a school project); non-response decreases reliability.

7. Populations

 1 (a) All the 30 boys
(b) Census
(c) Not a large population

2 (a) Any one from: completely accurate, opinion of all office managers considered, unbiased.
(b) Any two from: quicker, cheaper, easier, less data to handle.

3 List/database/register of the children

4 Only takes a sample of cars that are passing his house; only takes the sample on Monday morning; he might take the sample during morning rush hour.

8. Grouping data

1 $30 < x \leqslant 40$
$40 < x \leqslant 50$
$50 < x \leqslant 60$
$60 < x \leqslant 70$

2 $0 < x \le 1$
$1 < x \le 2$
$2 < x \le 3$
$3 < x \le 4$
$4 < x \le 5$
$5 < x \le 6$

3 (a) $50 < x \le 55$
$55 < x \le 60$
$60 < x \le 65$
$65 < x \le 70$
$70 < x \le 75$
$75 < x \le 80$
$80 < x \le 85$
$85 < x \le 90$

  (b) $x > 90$

9. Random sampling

1 In a random sample, all people/items have the same/equal chance/probability of selection.

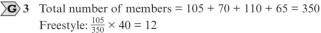

2 Number all the girls from 0 to 179.
Generate seven random numbers from a random number generator.
Girls with the generated numbers are selected for the sample.

3 (a) Each worker has an equal chance of being selected.
  (b) Number the workers from 0 to 1199.
The workers that correspond in her list are selected for the sample.
  (c) Not reliable as the sample size is small relative to the size of the total population.

4 Simple random sample.

10. Stratified sampling 1

1 (a) Method 1: Stratified. Method 2: Cluster
  (b) Any two from: more representative; random because it allows all members of the population an equal chance of representation; less biased; more reliable.

2 12

3 Total number of members = 105 + 70 + 110 + 65 = 350
Freestyle: $\frac{105}{350} \times 40 = 12$

Backstroke: $\frac{70}{350} \times 40 = 8$

Breaststroke: $\frac{110}{350} \times 40 = 12.6$, rounded up to 13

Butterfly: $\frac{65}{350} \times 40 = 7.4$, rounded down to 7

11. Non-random sampling

1 (a) Sample every 100th bolt.
Start at a random starting point between 1 and 100.
  (b) Any one from: not random, because each bolt does not have an equal chance of being selected; not representative because for example every 100th bolt may have the same defect.

2 (a) Advantage: any one from: quicker; easier; cheaper.
Disadvantage: any one from: not random; may be biased; may not be representative.
  (b) Cluster

3 (a) Quota
  (b) Advantage: any one from: convenient; easy; same number of men and women chosen; questions can be explained.
Disadvantage: any one from: takes time to reach a quota; biased; not random; may not be representative.

12. Stratified sampling 2

1 Total number of people = 84 + 64 + 95 + 48 + 32 + 77 = 400
$\frac{64}{\text{total}} = \frac{8}{\text{sample size}}$
Sample size = $8 \times \frac{400}{64} = 50$

Number of females under 18 = $\frac{48}{400} \times 50 = 6$

2 7

3 4

13. Petersen capture-recapture formula

1 $\frac{60}{n} = \frac{5}{60}$ so $n = \frac{60 \times 50}{6} = 500$

2 (a) 467
  (b) Assumption can include: the total number of ants does not change; ants are caught randomly; paint has not washed off.

3 (a) 72
  (b) Not reliable: the sample is too small; the time between the first and second samples is too short to allow the frogs to disperse fully in the lake.

14. Controlling extraneous variables 1

1 (a) Length of time
  (b) Number of calories used
  (c) Different speeds of the treadmill. All the people should run at the same speed.

2 (a) Music
  (b) Number of correct answers
  (c) Any two from: background noise – students can wear noise cancelling headphones; distractions such as people walking about – have a room with no windows; different ages – Year 7 students should be tested with other Year 7 students; students don't like the type of music – let the students choose their own music

3 Any two from: age of drivers – choose drivers of a similar age; experience of driving – choose drivers who have similar experience of driving; number of hours sleep required – some people may need more or less than 7 hours of sleep and some people may be insomniacs; beds – some people may not sleep well in a controlled environment as the bed may be different.

15. Controlling extraneous variables 2

1 Comparing a group having tea with one not having tea (the control group) helps to assess the effect of having tea.

2 (a) The control group is used to compare the patients who take the new drug with the patients who do not take the new drug.
  (b) The scientist gives either the new drug or no drug to each group of patients.
All the patients in both the groups have the same illness or condition.

3 (a) Match children with similar abilities in English.
  (b) Any method in which children in each pair are allocated randomly, e.g. get one child in each pair to toss a coin (and if they get heads then they get to learn the alphabet with diagrams).
  (c) Extraneous

16. Questionnaires and interviews 1

1 Any two from: no time frame; options overlap; no zero option.

2 Method 2/Questionnaire.
Any one of: Method 1 only allows those people already using the leisure centre to give their views; Method 1 is biased; Method 2 gives all residents the chance to say what they think; Method 2 is more reliable; Method 2 could mean more people participate; Method 2 (probably) uses a greater variety of people.

3 (a) Any one from: leading/biased question; open/no options given.

Answers

(b) Advantage: any one from: questions can be explained; better response rate.
Disadvantage: any one from: expensive; possible interviewer bias; interviewee might be under pressure; time consuming.

4 No units of distance; options are too vague.

17. Questionnaires and interviews 2

G 1 (a) Sensitive question or people do not want to answer it.
(b) $\frac{1}{2} \times 500 = 250$
(c) Estimate for the number who ticked box A who were truthful = 270 − 250 = 20
Estimate for the proportion of people who photocopied pages from textbooks illegally
$= \frac{20}{500 - 250} = \frac{20}{250} = \frac{2}{25} = 0.08 = 8\%$

18. Hypotheses

1 (a) It is a question.
(b) Variable 1: age of gas bottle. Variable 2: gas pressure
2 (a) The nearer the airport the lower the house price.
(b) Use the internet to find the house prices and to find distances from the houses to the airport.
3 (a) In Scotland, men get asthma at an earlier age than women.
(b) Any one from: it would be impossible to ask all the people who have asthma; it would be time consuming; it would be too costly; it would produce too much data to handle.

19. Designing investigations

G 1 (a) $\frac{250}{350} = \frac{600}{n}$ so $n = \frac{600 \times 350}{250} = 840$
(b) Advantage: any one from: people can give a more considered response/feel less pressured/take their time; avoids possible interviewer bias; ensures all questions get asked the same way; cheaper (no need to pay interviewers); faster way to collect lots of data.
Disadvantage: any one from: questions cannot be explained if not understood; may have many non-responses.
(c) Any two from: biased/leading question (says 'do you agree…'); open question (allows for too many different answers); no response boxes.
2 Any three from: stratified sampling is an appropriate method because it represents the population; stratified sampling is an appropriate method because it reduces bias; stratified sampling is not an appropriate method because the sample size is too small; stratified sampling is not an appropriate method because you should not stratify by the variable that you are investigating (age).

REPRESENTING DATA

20. Tables

1 (a) 24 600 (b) 25 210 (c) Upwards
2 (a) 2016 (b) 2019 (c) Upwards

21. Two-way tables

G 1

	Year group			Total
	Year 7	Year 9	Year 11	
Boys	215	126	115	456
Girls	100	132	201	433
Total	315	258	316	889

Total girls = 889 − 456 = 433
Year 9 boys = 258 − 132 = 126

Year 7 boys = 456 − 115 − 126 = 215
Year 7 girls = 315 − 215 = 100
Year 11 total = 889 − 315 − 258 = 316
Year 11 girls = 316 − 115 = 201

2 (a)

	Type of filling			Total
	Ham	Cheese	Tuna	
Boys	10	19	14	43
Girls	22	11	24	57
Total	32	30	38	100

(b) 32
(c) 43

3

	Subject			Total
	Mathematics	Physics	French	
Boys	28	16	17	61
Girls	23	6	10	39
Total	51	22	27	100

51 students like mathematics best.

22. Pictograms

G 1 (a) 18 cars
(b)

Month	Number of cars sold
April	
May	
June	
July	
August	

(c) Total = 24 + 32 + 18 + 12 + 36 = 122 so Sandeep is not correct.
2 (a) Key: ☐ represents 4 bouquets
(b) 5
(c) Four and a quarter rectangles

Month	Number of bouquets sold
Monday	
Tuesday	
Wednesday	
Thursday	
Friday	

23. Bar charts 1

1 (a)

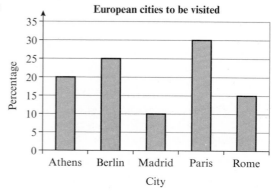

(b) Berlin
(c) Madrid

2 (a)

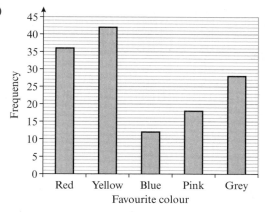

(b) Yellow (c) Pink

24. Bar charts 2

1 (a)

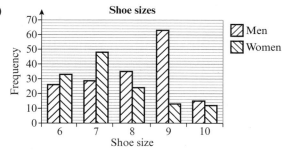

(b) 35
(c) 7
(d) More men than women
Men = 63 and women = 13

2 (a)

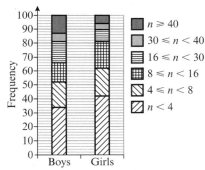

(b) Any two from: higher % of girls owned a computer for shorter periods, 52% boys and 62% girls owned a laptop for less than 8 months, 13% boys but only 6% girls owned a laptop for more than 40 months (or equivalents).

25. Stem and leaf diagrams

1

1	2 3 7
2	1 3 6 7
3	2 4 5 6 8
4	3 6 8

Key: 1|2 represents 12 miles

2 (a)

Before		After
8 5	5	
8 8 6 2 1 0	6	3 6 9
8 7 4 2 1	7	2 6 9
2 0	8	5 5 7 8
	9	1 3 7 8 9

Key : 0|6|3 represents 60 before and represents 63 after
(b) The heart rates increase after running (or equivalent).

26. Pie charts 1

1

Type of film	Number of adults	Angle of sector
Horror	18	90°
Animation	**13**	65°
Science fiction	21	**105°**
Thriller	**8**	40°
Foreign	**12**	**60°**

Horror: $\frac{90}{18}$ = 5° per adult

Animation: Number of adults $= \frac{65}{5} = 13$

Science fiction: Angle of sector = 21 × 5 = 105°

Thriller: Number of adults $= \frac{40}{5} = 8$

Foreign: Angle of sector = 360 − 90 − 65 − 105 − 40 = 60°

Foreign: Number of adults $= \frac{60}{5} = 12$

2 (a) (i) $\frac{90}{360} = \frac{1}{4}$

(ii) $\frac{50}{360} = \frac{5}{36}$

(b) 3
(c) 36

27. Pie charts 2

1 Apple: $\frac{20}{60} × 360 = 120°$

Carrot: $\frac{25}{60} × 360 = 150°$

Mango: $\frac{5}{60} × 360 = 30°$

Orange: $\frac{10}{60} × 360 = 60°$

Favourite fruit juice

2 Vehicles crossing bridge

28. Comparative pie charts

1 (a) Numbers have increased between 2005 and 2015.
The radius of the pie chart for 2015 is bigger than the pie chart for 2005.
(b) More adults in the age group 46–60 had laser treatment in 2015 than in 2005.
The area of the sector is bigger.

2 (a) Angle for LG in 2016 $= \frac{100}{450} × 360 = 80°$
(b) Total number of phones sold in 2017
= 216 + 172 + 179 + 315 = 882

$\frac{R^2}{r^2} = \frac{N}{n}$, so $R^2 = r^2 × \frac{N}{n}$

$R^2 = 5^2 × \frac{882}{450}$, so $R^2 = 49$, $R = \sqrt{49} = 7$ cm

29. Population pyramids

1 (a) (i) 20–29
    (ii) 50–59
 (b) 80–89

2 There is a greater percentage of young people in West Africa than in Western Europe; there is a lower percentage of old people in West Africa than in Western Europe.

30. Choropleth maps

G 1 (a)

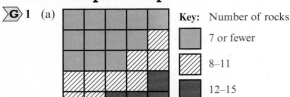

Key: Number of rocks
- 7 or fewer
- 8–11
- 12–15

 (b) The number of rocks increases as you move across to the right and down.

G 2 (a)

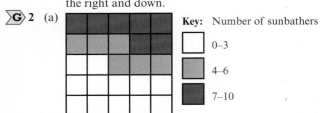

Key: Number of sunbathers
- 0–3
- 4–6
- 7–10

 (b) The number of sunbathers increases as you move across to the right and up.

31. Histograms and frequency polygons

G 1 (a), (b)

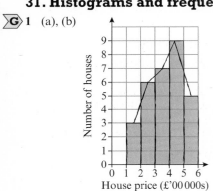

 (c) $4 < p \leqslant 5$

2 (a), (b)

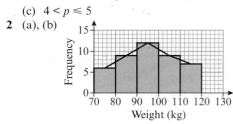

 (c) $90 < w \leqslant 100$
 (d) 28

32. Cumulative frequency diagrams 1

G 1 (a)

Weight (w g)	$80 < w \leqslant 90$	$90 < w \leqslant 100$	$100 < w \leqslant 110$
Frequency	6	14	17
Cumulative frequency	6	6 + 14 = 20	20 + 17 = 37

Weight (w g)	$110 < w \leqslant 120$	$120 < w \leqslant 130$
Frequency	29	14
Cumulative frequency	37 + 29 = 66	66 + 14 = 80

(b)

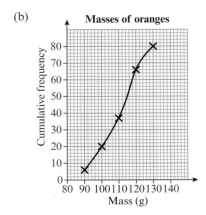

Masses of oranges

2 (a)

Distance (m miles)	$0 < m \leqslant 10$	$10 < m \leqslant 20$	$20 < m \leqslant 30$
Frequency	3	15	20
Cumulative frequency	3	18	38

Distance (m miles)	$30 < m \leqslant 40$	$40 < m \leqslant 50$	$50 < m \leqslant 60$
Frequency	36	20	6
Cumulative frequency	74	94	100

(b)

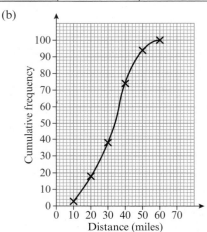

33. Cumulative frequency diagrams 2

G 1 (a) 45
 (b) 8

G 2 (a) Cumulative frequencies: 11, 39, 62, 81, 90

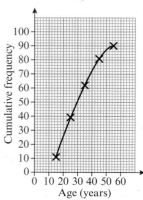

(b) Accept: 23–27
(c) Accept: 10–12

34. The shape of a distribution

1 (a)

Mason		Daisy
5 0 4 4 2	**2**	
7 4 5	**3**	5
1 2	**4**	3 7
0	**5**	7 4 1 3
	6	8 2 9 0

Mason		Daisy
5 4 4 2 0	**2**	
7 5 4	**3**	5
2 1	**4**	3 7
0	**5**	1 3 4 7
	6	0 2 8 9

Key: 2|4|3 represents 42 minutes for Mason,
4|3 represents 43 minutes for Daisy

(b) Mason's distribution has positive skew.
Daisy's distribution has negative skew.

2 (a), (b)

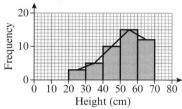

(c) Negative skew

35. Histograms with unequal class widths 1

1

Time, t (minutes)	$0 < t \le 15$	$15 < t \le 45$	$45 < t \le 60$	$60 < t \le 70$	$70 < t \le 90$
Frequency	30	135	75	38	12
Class width	15	30	15	10	20
Frequency density	$\frac{30}{15} = 2$	$\frac{135}{30} = 4.5$	$\frac{75}{15} = 5$	$\frac{38}{10} = 3.8$	$\frac{12}{20} = 0.6$

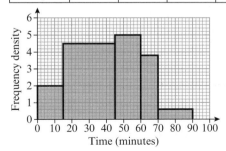

2

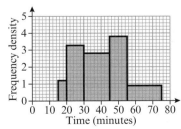

36. Histograms with unequal class widths 2

1 (a) Frequency density = $\frac{24}{5}$ = 4.8
Class width for $40 \le a < 50$ = 10
Frequency density for $40 \le a < 50$ = 3.1
Number of people in $40 \le a < 50$ class = 10 × 3.1 = 31

(b)

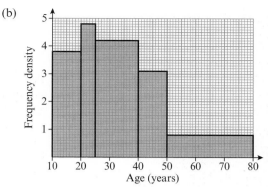

(c) Number of people in class $10 \le a < 20$ aged 16 or
over = $\frac{20 - 16}{10} \times 38$ = 15.2

Number of people in class $20 \le a < 25$ = 24
Number of people in class $25 \le a < 40$ aged 29 or
under = $\frac{29 - 25}{15} \times 63$ = 16.8

Total number of people who are between the ages of 16
and 29 = 15.2 + 24 + 16.8 = 56

2 $\frac{1}{7}$

37. Misleading diagrams

1 Any three from: missing label for one breed of dog; non-
linear scale (on vertical axis); bars different widths; missing
label (on vertical axis); missing zero; no title.

2 Any two from: bars are 3D; quarters are missing from the
horizontal axis; no label on either axis; no title.

3 Any three from: missing label on horizontal axis; no zero;
break in y-axis; no title; line is too thick.

38. Choosing the right format

1 (a) Not appropriate as the data is only taken in one
afternoon.
(b) Appropriate as the data is continuous.
(c) Not appropriate as the data is not bivariate.

2 (a) **B** because the data is not continuous.
(b) **A** because a pie chart shows a fraction of the total.

SUMMARISING DATA

39. Averages

1 (a) 3 hours
(b) Mean = $\frac{3 + 4 + 3 + 7 + 2 + 6 + 10}{7} = \frac{35}{7}$ = 5 hours
(c) Median = $\frac{7 + 1}{2}$th value = $\frac{8}{2}$ = 4th value, so choose the
4th value. Median = 5 hours.

2 (a) 19 km
(b) 17.25 km
(c) 18.5 km

3 (a) 19.05 kg
(b) 19.7 kg

40. Averages from frequency tables 1

1 (a) 2
(b)

Score	1	2	3	4	5	6
Frequency	7	12	5	11	7	8
Cum freq	7	19	24	35	42	50

Median = $\frac{50}{2}$th number = 25th number. Median score = 4

2 (a) This age occurs the most.
(b) 15 years

3 (a) 3 (b) 4

Answers

41. Averages from frequency tables 2

1 Mean $= \dfrac{(1 \times 7) + (2 \times 12) + (3 \times 4) + (4 \times 11) + (5 \times 7) + (6 \times 9)}{50}$

$= \dfrac{7 + 24 + 12 + 44 + 35 + 54}{50}$

$= \dfrac{176}{50}$

$= 3.52$

2 15.5 years

3 3.5

42. Averages from grouped data 1

1 (a) $10 < t \leqslant 20$

(b) $20 < t \leqslant 30$

(c) Total frequency = 50 so the median is the 25th value.

Estimated median $= 20 + \dfrac{25 - 15}{12} \times 10 = 20 + \dfrac{10}{12} \times 10$

$= 28.3$ minutes

2 (a) $8000 < x \leqslant 10\,000$

(b) $6000 < x \leqslant 8000$

(c) £6300

43. Averages from grouped data 2

1 (a)

Time taken (t minutes)	Frequency	Midpoint	f × midpoint
$10 < t \leqslant 20$	8	15	$8 \times 15 = 120$
$20 < t \leqslant 30$	14	25	$14 \times 25 = 350$
$30 < t \leqslant 40$	17	35	$17 \times 35 = 595$
$40 < t \leqslant 50$	12	45	$12 \times 45 = 540$
$50 < t \leqslant 60$	9	55	$9 \times 55 = 495$

Mean $= \dfrac{120 + 350 + 595 + 540 + 495}{60} = \dfrac{2100}{60}$

$= 35$ minutes

(b) The data is grouped.

2 13.1 miles

3 £20.27

44. Averages from grouped data 3

1 (a) Total frequency

$= 0.5 \times 10 + 2 \times 15 + 3 \times 5 + 2.5 \times 20 + 2 \times 10$

$= 5 + 30 + 15 + 50 + 20 = 120$

Median $= \dfrac{n}{2} = \dfrac{120}{2} = 60$th value

The median is in the interval 30–50.

Median $= 30 + \dfrac{60 - 50}{50} \times 20 = 30 + 4 = 34$ cm

(b)

Mean $= \dfrac{(5 \times 5) + (17.5 \times 30) + (27.5 \times 15) + (40 \times 50) + (55 \times 20)}{120}$

$= \dfrac{25 + 525 + 412.5 + 2000 + 1100}{120} = \dfrac{4062.5}{120} = 33.85$ cm

2 (a) 42.2 minutes (b) 46.1 minutes

45. Transforming data

1 (a) Monday (b) 50 visitors (c) 40 visitors

(d) Monday (e) 55 visitors (f) 44 visitors

2 (a) £64 000 (b) £65 920

46. Geometric mean

1 Geometric mean $= \sqrt[3]{25 \times 32 \times 68} = \sqrt[3]{54\,400} = 37.9$

2 1.21

3 (a) Geometric mean $= \sqrt{28\,475 \times 42\,380} = \sqrt{1\,206\,770\,500}$

$= £34\,739$

(b) £1390.50

---

4 1.08 or 8% annual increase

5 3.12

47. Weighted mean

1 (a) Mean $= \dfrac{65 + 89 + 60 + 62}{4} = \dfrac{276}{4} = 69$

(b) Weighted mean

$= \dfrac{(65 \times 30) + (89 \times 40) + (60 \times 20) + (62 \times 10)}{30 + 40 + 20 + 10}$

$= \dfrac{1950 + 3560 + 1200 + 620}{100}$

$= \dfrac{7330}{100} = 73.3$

(c) Test B has the highest marks (89) and the highest weighting (40%), so it has a large impact on the weighted mean. The other tests have lower weightings.

2 Salesman A (£601.90) > Salesman B (£484.13)

3 $x = 8$

48. Measures of dispersion for discrete data

1 (a) Range = highest value − lowest value

$= 18 - 7 = 11$ years

(b) Lower quartile $= \frac{1}{4}(15 + 1)$th = 4th value = 11

Upper quartile $= \frac{3}{4}(15 + 1)$th = 12th value = 14

Interquartile range = upper quartile − lower quartile

$= 14 - 11 = 3$ years

2 (a) 63 g (b) 17 g

(c) Does not take extreme values into account.

3 (a) 7 (b) 3

49. Measures of dispersion for grouped data 1

1 Range $= 70.5 - 19.5 = 51$ cm

2 (a) 24.2 kg (b) 39.2 kg

3 (a)

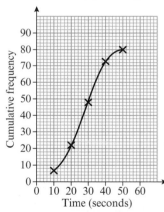

(b) 19–20 seconds (c) 34–35 seconds

50. Measures of dispersion for grouped data 2

1 (a) 70th percentile = 70% × 80th value = 56th value on the cumulative frequency axis

30th percentile = 30% × 80th value = 24th value on the cumulative frequency axis

$74 - 57 = 17$ seconds

(b) 23 seconds

(c) (i) 67 seconds (ii) The median time is 67 seconds.

2 (a) 115 km/h (b) 63.2 km/h

51. Standard deviation 1

1 (a) Mean $= \dfrac{324}{9} = 36$ points

(b) Standard deviation $= \sqrt{\dfrac{\Sigma p^2}{n} - \left(\dfrac{\Sigma p}{n}\right)^2} = \sqrt{\dfrac{11702}{9} - \left(\dfrac{324}{9}\right)^2}$

$= \sqrt{1300.2 - (36)^2} = \sqrt{1300.2 - 1296}$

$= \sqrt{4.2} = 2.05$ points

2 (a) $9.6^2 + 10.9^2 + 6.2^2 + 7.6^2 + 10.4^2 + 11.1^2 + 8.4^2 + 8.3^2$
$\quad + 6.9^2 + 7.6^2 + 6.9^2 + 10.1^2$
$\quad = 932.98$

    (b) 1.62 cm

3 (a) 1.80 m   (b) 0.42 m

52. Standard deviation 2

 1 Mean $= \dfrac{4810}{140} = 34.4$ miles

$\quad$ SD $= \sqrt{\dfrac{169775}{140} - \left(\dfrac{4810}{140}\right)^2} = \sqrt{1212.678\ldots - (34.357\ldots)^2}$

$\qquad = \sqrt{32.264\ldots} = 5.68$ miles

2 (a) 5.8 rooms   (b) 1.05 rooms

3 26.2 minutes

53. Standard deviation 3

 1 Mean $= \dfrac{\Sigma f x}{\Sigma f} = \dfrac{980}{125} = 7.84$ cm

$\quad$ Standard deviation $= \sqrt{\dfrac{\Sigma f x^2}{\Sigma f} - \left(\dfrac{\Sigma f x}{\Sigma f}\right)^2} = \sqrt{\dfrac{10126.25}{125} - \left(\dfrac{980}{125}\right)^2}$

$\qquad\qquad\qquad = \sqrt{81.01 - (7.84)^2} = \sqrt{19.544}$

$\qquad\qquad\qquad = 4.42$ cm

2 18.2 minutes

3 (a) 66.8 cm   (b) 27.7 cm

    (c) The midpoint of each interval is used as an estimate for the value of each data item in that interval, and not the exact data value. So, the mean and standard deviation calculated from this estimate are also estimates.

54. Box plots

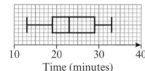 **1**

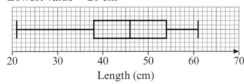 **2** Lower quartile $= \frac{1}{4}(15 + 1)$th $=$ 4th value $= 38$ cm
$\quad$ Median $= \frac{1}{2}(15 + 1)$th $=$ 8th value $= 46$ cm
$\quad$ Upper quartile $= \frac{3}{4}(15 + 1)$th $=$ 12th observation $= 54$ cm
$\quad$ Highest value $= 61$ cm
$\quad$ Lowest value $= 21$ cm

3

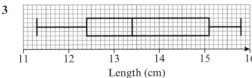

55. Outliers

 1 Mean $= \dfrac{\Sigma x}{n} = \dfrac{590}{15} = 39.33$ mm

$\quad$ Standard deviation $= \sqrt{\dfrac{\Sigma x^2}{n} - \left(\dfrac{\Sigma x}{n}\right)^2} = \sqrt{\dfrac{28\,068}{15} - (39.33\ldots)^2}$

$\qquad\qquad\qquad = \sqrt{324.4} = 18.01$ mm

$\quad$ Outliers are outside the range mean $\pm$ (3 $\times$ SD)
$\qquad = 39.33 - (3 \times 18.01)$ to $39.33 + (3 \times 18.01)$
$\qquad = -14.7$ to 93.36

$\quad$ Any values outside the range -14.7 to 93.36 are outliers, so 102 is an outlier.

2 (a) $47 - 1.5(60 - 47) = 27.5$ and $60 + 1.5(60 - 47) = 79.5$, so 23 is an outlier.

    (b)

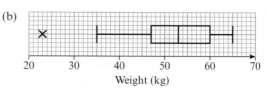

3 (a) $36 - 1.5(48 - 36) = 18$ and $48 + 1.5(48 - 36) = 66$, so 17 and 69 are outliers.

    (b)

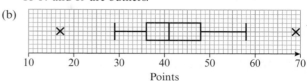

56. Skewness

1 Negative skew because median $-$ LQ $>$ UQ $-$ median

2 (a) Mean $= 13.4$, median $= 10$ and mode $= 2$

    (b) Positive skew

    (c) Generally, Tom is not very early for work.

3 (a) Negative skew

    (b) Generally, high numbered counters are drawn from the box.

57. Deciding which average to use

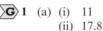 **1** (a) (i) 11

        (ii) 17.8

    (b) Median, because it is not affected by extreme values.

    (c) There is only one of each number.

2 One survey might measure the mean and the other survey might measure the median.

3 (a) Median   (b) Mean

4 No; the median is 41, mean is 41.1 and the mode is 40.

58. Comparing data sets

1 The median age is lower at Penn Surgery.
$\quad$ The IQR/range is greater at Himley Surgery.
$\quad$ On average the patients are younger at Penn Surgery.

2 Median is higher for Road X. Cars travel faster on Road X.
$\quad$ IQR is greater for Road Y.
$\quad$ Range is greater for Road X.

3 The mean is higher for music. Generally the music marks were higher (or the drama marks were lower).
$\quad$ The standard deviation is greater for drama. Generally the drama marks were more spread out (or the music marks were more consistent).

59. Making estimates

1 (a) 25%

    (b) (i) 130   (ii) 65

2 (a) 40%   (b) 600

3 £108

CORRELATION

60. Scatter diagrams

1 (a) A scatter diagram is suitable because this is bivariate data.

    (b)

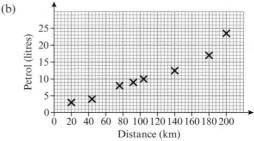

(c) Yes. As the distance increases the amount of petrol used increases.

2 (a) Hours of exercise because it is the explanatory variable.

(b)

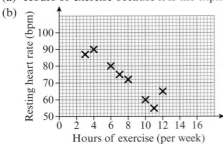

(c) Yes. As the number of hours of exercise increases the resting heart rate decreases.

61. Correlation

1 (a)

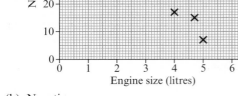

(b) Negative
(c) As the engine size increases the number of miles decreases.

2 As the maths mark increases the science mark increases.

62. Causal relationships

▷G 1 (a) There is probably a causal relationship between the maximum temperature and the number of hot chocolates sold because people like to drink hot chocolate in cold weather when the temperature is lower.

(b) The correlation is quite strong because temperature plays a part in the number of hot chocolates sold.

2 (a) Positive
(b) Probably not, as the length of a twig does not affect the length of a hand span.

63. Line of best fit

▷G 1 (a), (b)

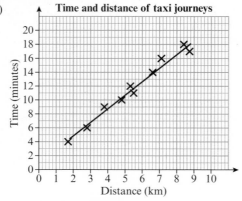

Time and distance of taxi journeys

(c) Any value between 5.8 km and 6.4 km.

2 (a), (c)

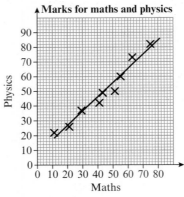

Marks for maths and physics

(b) Mean point = (43.25, 49.125)

64. Interpolation and extrapolation

1 (a), (c)

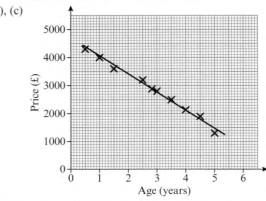

(b) Negative correlation. As the age increases the price decreases.
(d) (i) £3400–3600
(ii) It is reliable as the answer is within the data range (interpolation).
(e) (i) £650–850
(ii) It is not reliable as the answer is outside the data range (extrapolation).

65. The equation of a line of best fit 1

1 (a) The number of errors decreases as the numbers of minutes practised increases.
(b) −0.4
(c) (i) $y = -0.4x + 28$
(ii) a represents the number of errors (0.4) made for every 1 minute of extra practice. b represents the number of errors (28) when no practice is carried out.
(d) The estimate is outside the data range (extrapolation).

66. The equation of a line of best fit 2

▷G 1 (a) When $x = 170$, $y = 0.652 \times 170 - 13.6 = 97.24 \approx 97$

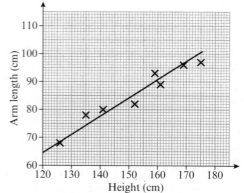

(b) For every increase of 1 cm in height, the arm length increases by 0.652 cm.

2 (a)

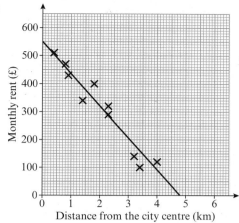

(b) For every increase of 1 km in distance from the centre, the rent decreases by £117.

(c) Monthly rent is −£620 which means the regression line is not a reliable predictor above the range of given values.

67. Spearman's rank correlation coefficient

 1 (a) Strong positive correlation
(b) Moderate negative correlation
(c) No correlation

2 Negative correlation, which means the longer John spent swimming the shorter his finish times.

3 Both scores show positive correlation. Rumba dancing scores had a stronger positive correlation than the correlation between the Salsa scores. Overall there is good agreement between Tom and Jerry.

68. Calculating Spearman's rank correlation coefficient

 1

Cake	A	B	C	D	E	F	G	H	I	J
Ravina	1	9	3	6	8	2	7	4	10	5
Anjali	8	4	7	1	3	5	10	9	6	2
d	7	5	4	5	5	3	3	5	4	3
d^2	49	25	16	25	25	9	9	25	16	9

$r_s = 1 - \dfrac{6\sum d^2}{n(n^2 - 1)}$

$= 1 - \dfrac{6 \times (49 + 25 + 16 + 25 + 25 + 9 + 9 + 25 + 16 + 9)}{10(10^2 - 1)}$

$= 1 - \dfrac{6 \times (208)}{990} = 1 - \dfrac{1248}{990}$

$= 1 - 1.26 = -0.26$

Weak negative correlation so disagreement between Ravina and Anjali.

2 $r_s = 0.786$
Strong positive correlation so good agreement between the critics.

69. Pearson's product moment correlation coefficient

 1 (a) SRCC = 0.85 and PMCC = 0.65
(b) PMCC is less strong as it measures closeness to a linear model, or PMCC is closer to 0 as graph does not suggest a straight line.

2 (a) SRCC is −0.87 and PMCC is −0.90
(b) No difference between the ranks of pairs of data so SRCC must be close to −1, or the graph is not a straight line so PMCC would not be close to −1.

TIME SERIES

70. Line graphs and time series

 1 (a)

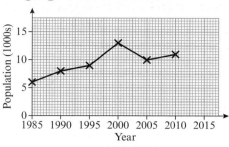

(b) (i) 2000 (ii) 7000

2 (a)

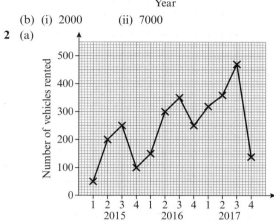

(b) More vehicles were rented in Q3/fewer vehicles were rented in Q4.

71. Trend lines

1 (a),(b)

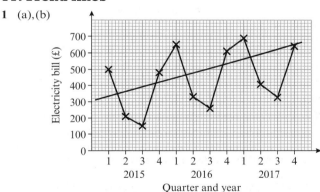

(c) The trend is upwards/rising.
The electricity bills are increasing with time.

2 (a), (b)

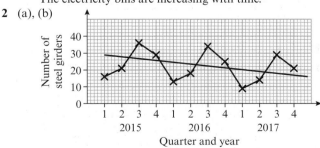

(c) The trend is downwards/falling.
The number of steel girders sold is decreasing with time.

72. Variations in a time series

1 (a), (b)

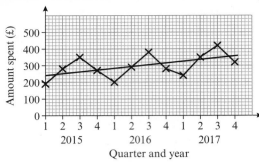

(c) The graph shows an increasing trend. The amount of money spent on cold drinks has increased over the three years. There is a seasonal variation, with the amount of money spent on cold drinks being higher than the trend value in the third quarter and lower in the first quarter. (More money is spent on cold drinks during the summer months or less money is spent on cold drinks in the winter months.)

2 (a)

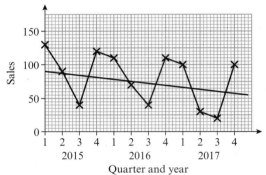

(b) The graph shows an decreasing trend. The sales of hot chocolate have decreased over the three years. There is a seasonal variation, with the sales of hot chocolates being higher than the trend value in the first quarter and lower in the third quarter. (Sales of chocolates are lower in the summer months or higher in the winter months.)

73. Moving averages 1

1 (a) 3275, 3225, 3075, 3025, 3000
(b) The moving averages show a downward trend such that the number of bolts made has decreased over the two years.

2 (a) 13, 18, 23, 24, 25, 27
(b) The moving averages show an upward trend such that the number of new cars sold has increased over this period of time.

74. Moving averages 2

1 (a), (b) (ii), (c)

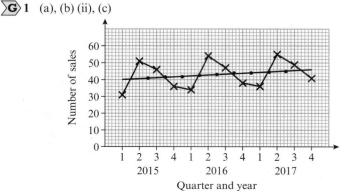

(b) (i) 43.75, 44, 44.5, 45.25
(d) Upward trend. Sales of motorbikes have increased.

75. Seasonal variations

1 (a), (b) (ii), (c)

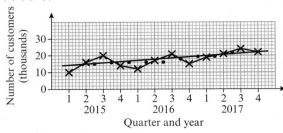

(b) (i) Missing values: 19.75, 21.5
(d) Quarter 1
(e) 20 500 − 20 800
(f) Not appropriate as the trend may not continue.

PROBABILITY

76. The meaning of probability 1

1 (a) (i) Certain (ii) Evens
(b)

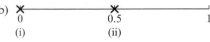

(i) (ii)

2 (a) likely
(b) impossible

3

Probability word	likely	evens	certain	unlikely	impossible
Probability	0.8	0.5	1	0.2	0

4

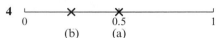

(b) (a)

77. The meaning of probability 2

1 (a) $P(A) = \dfrac{\text{number of successful outcomes}}{\text{total number of possible outcomes}} = \dfrac{4}{9}$
(b) $\frac{2}{9}$

2 (a) $\frac{3}{10}$ (b) 16

3 20

4 (a) $\frac{20}{60}$ or $\frac{1}{3}$ (b) 0 (c) $\frac{10}{60}$ or $\frac{1}{6}$

78. The meaning of probability 3

1 (a)

	Type of seating			
	Stalls	Circle	Balcony	Total
Adults	36	39	37	112
Children	41	21	31	93
Total	77	60	68	205

(b) 205
(c) (i) $P(\text{Child}) = \dfrac{\text{number of children}}{\text{total number of members}} = \dfrac{93}{205}$
(ii) $\frac{37}{205}$

2 (a)

	Monday	Wednesday	Friday	Total
Boys	15	12	16	43
Girls	21	22	14	57
Total	36	34	30	100

(b) (i) $\frac{36}{100}$ or $\frac{9}{25}$ (ii) $\frac{14}{100}$ or $\frac{7}{50}$ (iii) $\frac{34}{100}$ or $\frac{17}{50}$

79. Experimental probability

1 (a) $P(H) = \dfrac{\text{number of heads}}{\text{total number of flips}} = \dfrac{28}{45}$
(b) Repeat the experiment more times (or similar).

2 (a) $\frac{6}{30}$ or $\frac{1}{5}$

(b) Rebecca because the sample size is larger.

3 (a) $\frac{32}{50}$ or $\frac{16}{25}$

(b) Reliable since the conclusion is based on a large number of throws.

80. Using probability to assess risk

G 1 (a) Relative risk = $\dfrac{\text{risk for those in the group}}{\text{risk for those not in the group}}$

$= \dfrac{\frac{34}{90}}{\frac{4}{40}} = 0.3777... \div 0.1 = 3.78$ (3 s.f.)

(b) 0.292

2 (a) 1.5

(b) Relative risk is greater than 1 so Jenna is correct.

81. Sample space diagrams

G 1 (a)

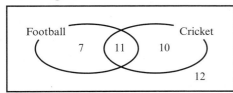

Dice B

	1	2	3	4	5	6
1	(1, 1)	(1, 2)	(1, 3)	(1, 4)	(1, 5)	(1, 6)
2	(2, 1)	(2, 2)	(2, 3)	(2, 4)	(2, 5)	(2, 6)
3	(3, 1)	(3, 2)	(3, 3)	(3, 4)	(3, 5)	(3, 6)
4	(4, 1)	(4, 2)	(4, 3)	(4, 4)	(4, 5)	(4, 6)
5	(5, 1)	(5, 2)	(5, 3)	(5, 4)	(5, 5)	(5, 6)
6	(6, 1)	(6, 2)	(6, 3)	(6, 4)	(6, 5)	(6, 6)

Dice A

(b) P(2, 3)

$= \dfrac{\text{number of ways getting 2 on one dice and 3 on the other}}{\text{total number of outcomes}}$

$= \dfrac{1+1}{36} = \dfrac{2}{36} = \dfrac{1}{18}$

(c) $\frac{5}{36}$

(d) Probability of getting a score of 9 is greater than the probability of getting a score of 4. $P(4) = \frac{3}{36}$, $P(9) = \frac{4}{36}$

2 (a)

5-sided spinner

	2	4	6	8	10
1	3	5	7	9	11
2	4	6	8	10	12
3	5	7	9	11	13
4	6	8	10	12	14

4-sided spinner

(b) (i) $\frac{2}{20}$ or $\frac{1}{10}$ (ii) $\frac{8}{20}$ or $\frac{2}{5}$

82. Venn diagrams

G 1 (a)

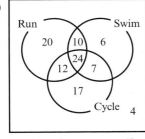

Football 7 (11) 10 Cricket

12

(b) (i) $\frac{7}{40}$ (ii) $\frac{10}{40}$ or $\frac{1}{4}$ (iii) $\frac{17}{40}$ (iv) $\frac{12}{40}$ or $\frac{3}{10}$

2 (a)

Run 20 (10) 6 Swim

24

12 7

17

Cycle 4

(b) (i) $\frac{4}{100}$ or $\frac{1}{25}$ (ii) $\frac{13}{100}$

83. Mutually exclusive and exhaustive events

G 1 (a) When two events cannot happen at the same time.

(b) (i) P(10 or 30) = $\dfrac{2+4}{10} = \dfrac{6}{10}$ or $\dfrac{3}{5}$ (ii) $\dfrac{7}{10}$

2 Yes, because the probabilities add up to 1.

3 (a) 0.36   (b) 0.34   (c) 0.70

84. The general addition law

G 1 P(A or B) = P(A) + P(B) − P(A and B)
= 0.35 + 0.45 − 0.12 = 0.68

2 (a) 0.5   (b) 0.2

3 (a) 0.8   (b) 0.7

4 (a) 0.42   (b) 0.21

5 0.05

85. Independent events

G 1 (a) P(A and B) = P(A) × P(B) = 0.2 × 0.65 = 0.13

(b) 0.72

2 (a) $\frac{49}{144}$

(b) $\frac{70}{144} = \frac{35}{72}$

3 (a) 0.12

(b) P(A) × P(B) = 0.12
P(A and B) = 0.12
Hence, P(A and B) = P(A) × P(B)

4 (a) 0.7 × 0.55 = 0.385

(b) 0.385 ≠ 0.25 Not independent

86. Tree diagrams

G 1 (a)

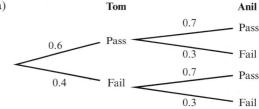

Tom   Anil

0.6 Pass — 0.7 Pass
            0.3 Fail
0.4 Fail — 0.7 Pass
            0.3 Fail

(b) P(Tom fails) = 1 − 0.6 = 0.4
P(Anil fails) = 0.3
P(Tom fails and Anil fails) = 0.4 × 0.3 = 0.12

(c) 0.46

2 (a)

Chicken   Weight

0.35 Organic — 0.1 Not sold
                0.9 Sold
0.65 Standard — 0.15 Not sold
                0.85 Sold

(b) 0.1325

(c) 0.264

87. Conditional probability

G 1 (a)

		Right handed	Left handed	Ambidextrous	Total
Gender	**Boys**	30	38	16	84
	Girls	8	48	30	86
	Total	38	86	46	170

(b) $\frac{48}{170}$ or $\frac{24}{85}$

(c) $\frac{30}{38}$ or $\frac{15}{19}$

(d) $\frac{30}{86}$ or $\frac{15}{43}$

2 (a)

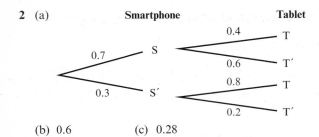

(b) 0.6   (c) 0.28

88. The formula for conditional probability

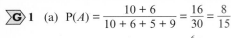**1** (a) $P(A) = \dfrac{10 + 6}{10 + 6 + 5 + 9} = \dfrac{16}{30} = \dfrac{8}{15}$

(b) $P(A \mid B) = \dfrac{P(A \text{ and } B)}{P(B)} = \dfrac{\frac{6}{30}}{\frac{11}{30}} = \dfrac{6}{11}$

(c) $\dfrac{8}{15} \neq \dfrac{6}{11}$ Not independent

2 (a) 0.15

(b) 0.375

3 (a)

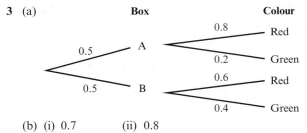

(b) (i) 0.7   (ii) 0.8

INDEX NUMBERS

89. Index numbers

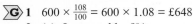**1** $600 \times \dfrac{108}{100} = 600 \times 1.08 = £648$

2 (a) Increased by 9%

(b) 98.5

3 (a) 102.4

(b) Both increased
NI increased by 2.4% and Scotland increased by 5.6%

90. RPI and CPI

1 2005 to 2010:
Percentage increase in RPI = 116% − 100% = 16%

Percentage increase in travel card price
$= \dfrac{36.80 - 30.40}{30.40} \times 100 = 21\%$

2005 to 2015:
Percentage increase in RPI = 135% − 100% = 35%
Percentage increase in travel card price
$= \dfrac{46.10 - 30.40}{30.40} \times 100 = 52\%$

RPI increased by 16% from 2005 to 2010 and the travel card price increased by 21% so the travel card price increased more than the RPI.

RPI increased by 35% from 2005 to 2015 and the travel card price increased by 52% so the travel card price increased more than the RPI.

2 CPI increased by 14% from 2005 to 2010 and the calculator price increased by 17% so the price increased more than the CPI.
CPI increased by 28% from 2005 to 2015 and the calculator price increased by 25% so the price increased less than the CPI.

3 RPI increased by 77%, CPI increased by 60% and stamp price increased by 77% so the price increase follows the RPI.

91. GDP

1 (a) (i) Q2 and 2014   (ii) Q2 and 2016

(b) 0.775%, 0.525%, 0.425% so 2014 had the greatest average growth.

2 (a) Upwards (or similar)   (b) Tunisia   (c) 2008

3 No, because manufacturing is 10 times larger than agriculture. The 0.3% increase in manufacturing is larger than the 0.4% increase in agriculture because manufacturing is 10 times larger than agriculture.

92. Weighted index numbers

1 (a) Weighted index number $= \dfrac{\sum wx}{\sum w} = \dfrac{(65 \times 92) + (35 \times 87)}{65 + 35}$

$= \dfrac{5980 + 3045}{100}$

$= \dfrac{9025}{100} = 90.25$

(b) 9.75 % decrease in production

2 Weighted index number = 105.405 so an increase of 5.405% Company is correct.

3 (a) Weighted mean for 2017 is £53 and weighted mean for 2018 is £60.80
Index number for 2018 = 114.7

(b) 14.7% increase in the weighted mean cost

93. Chain base index numbers

1 (a) Percentage increase = 114.3 − 100 = 14.3%

(b) Chain base index number for 2017 $= \dfrac{2600}{2400} \times 100$

$= 1.08333 \times 100$
$= 108.3$ to 1 d.p.

Chain base index number for 2018 $= \dfrac{2900}{2600} \times 100$

$= 1.11538 \times 100$
$= 111.5$ to 1 d.p.

(c) Geometric mean $= \sqrt[3]{114.3 \times 108.3 \times 111.5} = 111.3$

(d) Average price increase of 11.3% per year

2 (a)

Month	Jan	Feb	Mar	Apr	May
Value (£)	21 000	20 000	18 400	18 000	17 800
Chain base index number		95.2	92.0	97.8	98.9

(b) 95.9

(c) Average price decrease of 4.1% per month

94. Crude rates

1 (a) (i) Crude death rate $= \dfrac{260}{25\,000} \times 1000 = 10.4$

(ii) 8.6

(b) 24 955   (c) 180

2 (a)

Age group	Wells		
	Population	Deaths	Death rate
Under 16	1125	4	3.6
16–40	3000	20	6.7
41–70	7500	120	16
Over 70	2250	170	75.6

(b) Total population = 1125 + 3000 + 7500 + 2250 = 13 875

Crude death rate $= \left(3.6 \times \dfrac{1125}{13\,875}\right) + \left(6.7 \times \dfrac{3000}{13\,875}\right)$

$+ \left(16 \times \dfrac{7500}{13\,875}\right) + \left(75.6 \times \dfrac{2250}{13\,875}\right)$

$= (3.6 \times 0.0811) + (6.7 \times 0.2162)$
$+ (16 \times 0.5405) + (75.6 \times 0.1622)$

$= 0.29196 + 1.44854 + 8.648$
$+ 12.26232 = 22.7$ to 1 d.p.

(c) The crude death rate for Wells is higher than for Pennhouse. This can be seen from the actual population numbers in each age group. Wells has an older population whereas in Pennhouse the majority are under 40.

95. Standardised rates

 1 (a) Under 16 age group: $\frac{6}{3000} \times 1000 = 2$

16–35 age group: $\frac{18}{12000} \times 1000 = 1.5$

36–65 age group: $\frac{8}{10000} \times 1000 = 0.8$

Over 65 age group: $\frac{60}{4000} \times 1000 = 15$

Standardised death rate = death rate × standard population

Standardised death rate = $(2 \times 0.25) + (1.5 \times 0.35)$
$+ (0.8 \times 0.3) + (15 \times 0.1)$
$= 0.5 + 0.525 + 0.24 + 1.5$
$= 2.8$ to 1 d.p.

(b) The standardised death rate makes comparisons with other villages possible.

(c) Eastside because the standardised death rate is lower than in Westside.

96. Binomial distributions 1

 1 (a) $\frac{9}{14} \times \frac{9}{14} = \frac{81}{196}$

(b) P(Different colours)
= P(White and black) + P(Black and white)
$= \left(\frac{9}{14} \times \frac{5}{14}\right) + \left(\frac{5}{14} \times \frac{9}{14}\right) = \frac{45}{196} + \frac{45}{196} = \frac{90}{196} = \frac{45}{98}$

2 0.42

3 0.455

4

X	0	1	2
P(X)	0.09	0.42	0.49

97. Binomial distributions 2

 1 (a) Any two of: fixed number of customer calls; customer calls are independent; there are two possible outcomes – sale or no sale; the probability of making a sale is constant from call to call.

(b) 0.32768

(c) 0.05792

2 (a) 2

(b) 0.268

(c) 0.677–0.678

(d) $1 - 0.8^n$
$n = 14$
The smallest value of n is 14.

98. Normal distributions

1

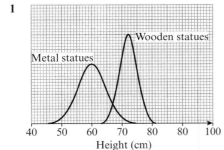

Metal statues | Wooden statues

Height (cm)

2 (a) Normal distribution because the data is continuous.

(b) (i) 0.68

(ii) 0.025

(c) 5

99. Standardised scores

 1 Mean $= \frac{\Sigma x}{n} = \frac{5400}{60} = 90$

Standard deviation $= \sqrt{\frac{\Sigma x^2}{n} - \left(\frac{\Sigma x}{n}\right)^2} = \sqrt{\frac{489\,840}{60} - \left(\frac{5400}{60}\right)^2}$
$= \sqrt{8164 - (90)^2} = \sqrt{8164 - 8100}$
$= \sqrt{64}$
$= 8$

Standardised score $= \frac{\text{mark} - \text{mean}}{\text{standard deviation}} = \frac{78 - 90}{8}$
$= \frac{-12}{8}$
$= -1.5$

2 (a) 0.8

(b) Asha, because her standardised score is higher.

(c) 118 m

3 (a) 1.75

(b) Jess did better in the javelin because the standardised score was higher.

100. Quality assurance and control charts 1

1 (a), (b) (i)

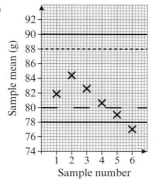

(b) (ii) Stop the machines and reset.

2

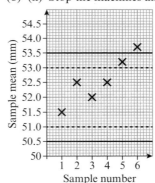

Sample 5 is between the warning and action limit lines. Take another sample.

Sample 6 is above the upper action limit so stop the machines and reset.

101. Quality assurance and control charts 2

1 (a) Take another sample (immediately)

(b) (i) 4.2

(ii)

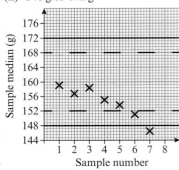

(iii) Stop the machine and reset.

2 (a) (i) 152 g to 168 g

(ii) 148 g to 172 g

(b)

Sample 7 is below the lower action limit line so stop the machine and reset.